A Delight of Owls

PETER STEYN

A DELIGHT OF OWLS
African Owls Observed

TANAGER BOOKS Dover, New Hampshire

DAVID PHILIP Cape Town & Johannesburg

First published 1984 in Southern Africa by David Philip, Publisher (Pty) Ltd, 217 Werdmuller Centre, Claremont, Cape, 7700 South Africa; and in the United States of America by Tanager Books, Inc., Washington Street, Dover, New Hampshire 03820

Distributed in the United Kingdom and Europe by Global Book Resources Ltd, 109 Great Russell Street, London WC1B 3NA

ISBN 0 86486 030 7 (David Philip)
ISBN 0-88072-063-8 (Tanager Books)

Library of Congress Cataloging in Publication Data

Steyn, Peter.
  A delight of owls.

  Bibliography: p.
  Includes index.
    1. Owls. 2. Birds——Africa, Southern. I. Title.
QL696.S8S744 1985   598'.97'0968   84-24111
ISBN 0-88072-063-8 (Tanager Books)

Printed and bound by Printpak (Cape) Ltd, Dacres Avenue, Epping, Cape, South Africa

Contents

To JEN-WREN

as delightful as any owl

Foreword by Eric Hosking

In 1961 Peter and Jenny Steyn visited us here in England and ever since then we have been firm friends. In 1972 my wife, our son David and I went to stay with them in Rhodesia and there can be no doubt that what impressed us more than anything else was his love and knowledge of birds and his enthusiasm for photographing them.

There are two types of bird photographer: the one puts the bird first and if he sees that it is under stress will stop photography immediately; the other is the *photographer* of birds who thinks only of the photographic results and cares little or nothing about what happens to the bird or its young. The *bird* photographer makes careful notes on the behaviour of his subject, the food it brings to the nest, its attention to the young, its displays, and indeed everything of interest—as well as his photographs. Peter keeps copious notes and uses his camera as a servant, not a master, to illustrate patterns of behaviour, although he is not averse to taking portraits. Working at night on owls means that you cannot see to identify the food brought to the nest, but the camera, with the aid of flash, does this for you.

The author deals with all twelve species of owls found in southern Africa and has managed to photograph nine of them at the nest. Of the remaining three, Scops he has photographed at a roost, Marsh he kept in captivity (a beautiful bird in immaculate condition that he had while we were staying with him), and the elusive Pel's Fishing Owl he has watched but never successfully photographed, so he has included striking pictures taken by a friend. Peter is almost certainly the first and only person to have photographed the Barred Owl and Cape (Mackinder's) Eagle Owl at their nests. In addition to his photographs, the author has contributed much to our knowledge of southern African birds, not least the owls, and particularly the life histories of Barn, Wood, Pearl-spotted, Barred and Cape Eagle Owls. Having spent some fifty-four years of my life photographing birds, I know just how difficult it is to photograph and make notes, especially at night.

Of all the world's owls the Barn Owl is my favourite, so I was particularly interested in the detailed chapter on this species. By having a pair breeding in his garden he was able to make an intimate study of them, which makes fascinating reading. I always used to think that Peter's favourite bird was the Black, or Verreaux's, Eagle; if it is, then the Barn Owl must surely run it a close second. His *Birds of Prey of Southern Africa*, published in 1982, shows his wide knowledge of raptors, but it is more of a reference book than one to be read from cover to cover. In a sense *A Delight of Owls* is a nocturnal version of his earlier book *Eagle Days*, which is light and readable, so that he communicates the pleasure of his experiences to the ordinary reader.

The photographs add immeasurably to the pleasure of this book, indeed one can look at them again and again. To those who might think that bird photography involves just sitting in a hide clicking away I would suggest they look at the photographs of hides erected for owls nesting high up in trees or other difficult situations. Not only must you find your nest, often no simple task, but then the materials have to be transported to the site, sometimes over long distances and rough country. Finding your way back from the nesting site after dark can also be a difficult and eerie experience. The outstanding photographs in this book give little indication of the work that has gone into obtaining them.

It has given me the greatest possible pleasure to write the Foreword to this delightful book and I sincerely hope it enjoys the success it so richly deserves.

ERIC HOSKING
London

Acknowledgements

It is always gratifying to thank those who have given one help, and over a period of some thirty years I have received generous assistance, hospitality and encouragement from many people, indeed it is an invidious task to try to remember them all.

Eric Hosking has contributed a Foreword and there is no one more suitable. His own lifelong passion for owls is well known and his many published photographs did much to kindle my enthusiasm. He has also given me much encouragement over the years. Without the assistance of the late Douglas Ncube many of my objectives would have been difficult to achieve. He became a companion rather than an assistant and I dedicated *Birds of Prey in Southern Africa* to his memory. Dave Tredgold features in several chapters and his contribution has been considerable, but above all he was a good friend with whom to share experiences. The late Dr Gerry Broekhuysen encouraged me as a boy and his widow Mariette generously permitted me to have access to his unpublished book on the life of the Spotted Eagle Owl. Without the aid of Tim Liversedge my chapter on Pel's Fishing Owl would have been somewhat bleak. My former colleague at Falcon College, John Stakesby–Lewis, organised the expedition to the Okavango Swamps, where we found a Barred Owl's nest.

The help of friends greatly enhanced my knowledge of several species: Josephine Scott shared her Wood Owls with me; Alex Masterson and Steve Lees showed me nests of the Grass Owl; the Pearl-spotted Owl nesting in Cliff Freeman's garden was co-operative and delightful; Val Gargett and Hans Grobler helped with the Cape Eagle Owl; Dave Barbour found an ideal White-faced Owl's nest; Ian Macdonald enabled me to observe and photograph the Giant Eagle Owl; and Nico Myburgh found a perfect Spotted Eagle Owl's nest just in time for photographs to be included in this book.

The nest of a Scops Owl has eluded me, and Alan Weaving has generously permitted the use of his photographs. As far as I know he is the only person to have photographed it at the nest. Graeme Arnott has contributed a line drawing based on one of Tim Liversedge's slides of a Pel's Fishing Owl making a kill.

The following have assisted in various ways and I am deeply grateful to them: Stephen Baron, Phyl Beaumont, Richard Brooke, the late Leslie Brown, Michael Irwin, Alan Kemp, Walter Mangold, Rob Martin, John Mendelsohn, Mike Mylne, Terry Oatley, Richard Peek, Elliot Pinhey, Barrie and Elaine Pryce, Alistair Robertson, Geoff Robin, Douglas and Olive–Mary Robinson, Peter Smith, Warwick Tarboton, Bob Thomson, the late Vic Tuer, Viv Wilson, and numerous members of the Falcon College Natural History Society.

Finally, but by no means least in importance, I thank my family. At one stage or another they were pressed into service to catch grasshoppers, set mousetraps at night when I was away, or generally to care for our captive owls. Above all Jenny (Jen-Wren to us) typed the text (her third book) and never begrudged her husband's enthusiasm for owls. I count myself fortunate that she was not like Lady Macduff's wren:

> . . . *for the poor wren,*
> *The most diminutive of birds, will fight,*
> *Her young ones in her nest, against the owl.*

Introduction

I make no apology for the title of this book. There are many unusual 'nouns of assembly' and 'a hoot of owls' is one of them. While some owls do hoot, there are many which do not, and their calls are often as weird as they are varied. Therefore I have coined 'a delight of owls', for no one can argue that there is any owl that is not delightful, and a collection of owls can only compound their delightfulness.

It requires a certain peculiar blend of enthusiasm, dedication and masochism to sit up 'in the dead vast and middle of the night' studying owls. An immediate problem is a visual one; the observer can see very little without the aid of artificial light, while the owl's vision is perfect and its hearing usually acute. Not only does one need to have effective concealment within a hide, but also the ability to remain immobile for long periods; on two occasions I have had mice nibbling at my shoelaces.

This book was written in Cape Town, where the number of owl species is limited, and the process evoked a deep nostalgia for those days in the bushveld of what was then Rhodesia, where most of my material was gathered. It seemed fitting to refer in the text to Rhodesia because I left before it became Zimbabwe. Also I have used the Rhodesian place names as I knew them then, but wherever one has since changed I have placed the new version in brackets after its original name when this is first mentioned. At the time of writing, very few of the new names are generally known and are unlikely to be found on maps presently available. However, when discussing the distribution of owls, it was obviously appropriate to refer to Zimbabwe.

As is evident from various chapters my interest in owls began when I was a boy in Cape Town, but it was only when I qualified as a teacher and went to settle in Rhodesia in 1961 that I was able to study and photograph any of them in detail. The first nine years of my sixteen years there were spent at Falcon College near Bulawayo, a school in the bushveld where my ornithological interests assumed a new dimension. There was just too much to do and I often regret many neglected opportunities. When I 'retired' from schoolmastering to follow my interests on a full-time basis my horizons expanded considerably, but as is so often the case there was never enough time to do all that I wanted, so when I returned to Cape Town in 1977 there were still many things left undone. But I look back on my Rhodesian days as the most enjoyable and productive of my life.

In his Foreword Eric Hosking has described *A Delight of Owls* as a nocturnal version of my first book *Eagle Days*. This is apposite because my purpose remains the same—to communicate my enjoyment, especially to those who do not have much knowledge of owls. In the text I have recalled the thrill of my first sighting of each species, something that remains forever vivid. Inevitably there is repetition of information contained in *Birds of Prey of Southern Africa*, but there I was writing a strictly functional 'tight' text while here I can indulge many of the anecdotes from behind the scenes. In the course of studying owls I have been privileged to contribute new knowledge on several species, but where there are some rather technical details, as in the study of the Barn Owl, I have confined them to appendices at the back of the book. An aspect that I have found striking is the contribution of amateurs to our knowledge of owls, and this emerges in a number of places in the text.

Except where relevant to my account, I have not dealt with the various physical attributes that go towards making an owl what it is—one could write a chapter on eyesight alone—and readers should consult the general bibliography for books that give these details. I have also included a section of specific references, so that certain remarks in the text, or studies referred to, may be traced to their source. As these references are relevant rather than comprehensive, *Birds of Prey of Southern Africa* should be consulted for a more detailed list of citations.

Africa is rich in owls: there are nine genera comprising thirty-one species, although two of these are marginal and one a migrant. This book deals with the twelve species found in southern Africa but none is endemic to this region and most are widely distributed elsewhere in Africa. Many of our African owls are virtually unknown, indeed one species, the Sokoke Scops Owl, was discovered as recently as 1965. The order of the chapters does not adhere strictly to current check-list usage: I have dealt with the Marsh Owl before the Wood Owl so as to link it with its ecological counterpart the Grass Owl; it was also logical and convenient to discuss the Spotted Eagle Owl before the Cape Eagle Owl. I hope that female readers will forgive the fact that my captive owls are always males; the reason is that owls are difficult to sex, so I always treated them as masculine, a purely arbitrary decision.

Some details of the techniques required when observing and photographing owls at night may prove of use to other strigiphiles, if I may coin a name for a lover of owls. The first essential is a hide (or blind). I use a collapsible aluminium framework with a strong canvas cover. It is useful to have a couple of projecting 'arms' clamped onto the front crossbar of the hide. Then, by using sliding brackets, one can attach flash heads at the required distance from the nest. If the site is on the ground, or level with the top of a bank as in the case of the Wood Owl, then the task is relatively easy. However, if the nest is at some height in a tree, then I use an aluminium scaffolding with a floor at the top onto which the hide is placed. Sometimes one has to improvise, as in the case of the hide built on the water tower in my garden in Bulawayo to photograph the Barn Owl, or the hide built amongst the rafters in a derelict house, also for the Barn Owl. I do not normally like to use a motorised camera operated remotely, but for the Giant Eagle Owl this technique was used with success.

Most of the pictures in this book were taken with a Hasselblad 500C camera; it has the advantage of a large format and interchangeable magazines. The latter facility is particularly useful because by simply changing the backs one can take both black-and-white and colour without moving the camera. Also, if one has spare magazines, the awkward business of loading film at night is obviated. The Hasselblad's only drawback is its noisy shutter operation. Electronic flash is essential and it is usually best to use two heads set slightly apart to eliminate shadows. I am often asked whether the bright flash doesn't upset one's subject, but almost invariably owls take little notice when it goes off. Far more important is to avoid noise or movement, hence the necessity to sit still for long periods. A creaking stool, or the rustle of a sandwich packet being undone, can easily scare off a sensitive species like the Barn Owl. When I first photographed an owl at the nest I chose a night when the moon was full. Later I found that owls are remarkably tolerant of the beam of a spotlight focused on the nest. Initially I covered the reflector with red cellophane, but subsequently I found it was not necessary and that owls would tolerate a full beam. In the case of the Barred Owl I hung a gas lamp near the nest.

A word of caution. Some owls do attack, and it is never safe to assume that a particular species is always docile. Quite often Spotted Eagle Owls nesting on buildings lose their fear of people and attack readily. The silent flight of an owl means that it strikes without warning, so it is always wise to protect one's eyes and wear some protective headgear. A friend once went rather far in response to my advice and came dressed like a First World War air ace, so we called him 'The Red Baron'. But Eric Hosking lost an eye to a Tawny Owl, which gave him an ideal title for his autobiography *An Eye for a Bird*. He once told me, with a twinkle in his remaining eye, that it was a title which could be interpreted in *three* ways.

For obvious reasons owls are difficult creatures to study, but to me this is part of their attraction. It requires some endurance to sit overnight for thirteen hours, as I did on two occasions with a Cape Eagle Owl, but the rewards far outweigh the discomforts, indeed the latter are soon forgotten. Owls are intrinsically fascinating for a number of reasons, and to the strigiphile they are pure delight. I hope that in the following pages the reader will share in my delight.

List of colour plates

PLATE 1

The Barn Owl that nested on the water tower in the garden in Bulawayo (p. 20).

PLATE 2

This series shows the development of nestling Barn Owls (see p. 19 and Appendix 1). Here they are 8, 5 and 3 days old.

The nestlings at 22, 19, 17 and 12 days old.

The brood at 29–19 days old.

The young at 43–36 days old; only the youngest is still mainly downy, but it had caught up to its siblings in weight.

This view of the Marandellas Grass Owl's nest in bracken shows the nestlings at a month old (p. 37).

At six weeks old the nestling Grass Owl is still mainly downy.

By the time it is seven weeks old it is well feathered above but still downy on the underparts.

Once fully feathered the young Grass Owl is washed with tawny-buff on the face and breast.

PLATE 4

A portrait of the Marsh Owl reared in my aviary in Bulawayo (p. 46).

This study of a young Marsh Owl shows its rather woebegone expression.

PLATE 6

After many unsuccessful attempts I eventually obtained this picture of the Chipinga Wood Owl alighting with an insect in its bill (p. 54).

PLATE 7

The Chipinga Wood Owl brought in a colourful hawk moth for its chicks.

PLATE 8

Portrait of a young captive White-faced Owl.

A study of 'Love', the captive White-faced Owl, with a mouse (p. 62).

PLATE 9

This roosting Scops Owl uses shadow as an effective camouflage (p. 64).

The same owl photographed with flash-light.

I was able to lure this Scops Owl within photographic range by playing it a tape-recording of its own call (p. 64).

PLATE 10

A Pearl-spotted Owl photographed at Robins Camp in Wankie National Park; note the large feet (p. 73).

PLATE 11

This picture of 'Pearly' the
captive Pearl-spotted Owl
gives a good indication of
his small size.

A portrait of 'Pearly' in a
more natural environment.

PLATE 12

'Oliver' the Barred Owl at a month old . . .

. . . and several weeks later once fully
feathered (p. 84).

A portrait of 'Oliver' the Barred Owl as he was about to pounce on prey.

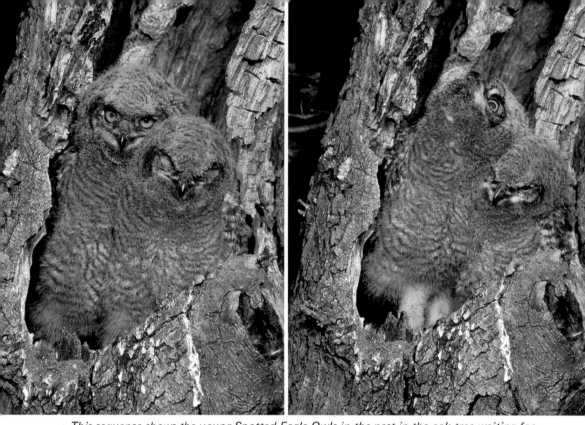

This sequence shows the young Spotted Eagle Owls in the nest in the oak tree waiting for their first meal of the evening (p. 104).

PLATE 15

The female Spotted Eagle Owl brings in a
decapitated dove . . .

. . . and later a mole, a picture I had
dreamed of for thirty years (p. 105).

The female Spotted Eagle Owl brooding her young with one wing hanging down to reveal the attractive pattern of markings (p. 105).

PLATE 17

The female Spotted Eagle Owl brings in a guineafowl chick . . .

. . . which is swallowed whole (p. 106).

This sequence shows the young Spotted Eagle Owl struggling to swallow the hindquarters of a large rat; on its eighth attempt it was eventually successful (p. 104).

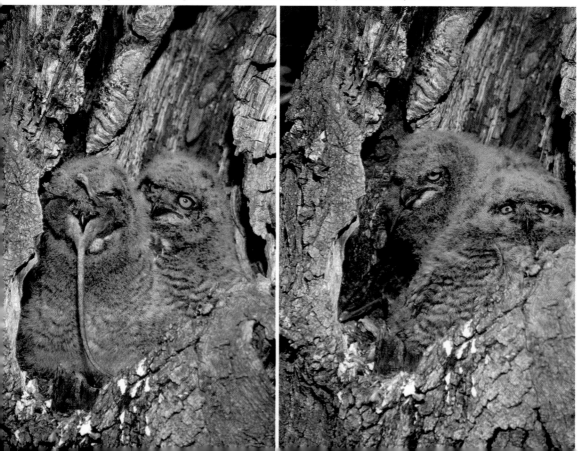

An exciting find—the nest and eggs of the elusive Cape Eagle Owl at Shangani (p. 111).

The Cape Eagle Owl nestlings at 8 and 4 days old; a dassie and the feathers of a Speckled Pigeon lie in the nest (p. 116).

The nestlings at 19 and 15 days old; a young dassie and a young hare provide more food than they can eat in a single night at this age.

The young owls at 55 and 51 days old, showing their large feet.

PLATE 20

The female Cape Eagle Owl—the first time the species had been photographed at the nest at night (p. 117).

A typical posture as she feeds her owlet.

With her 19-day-old owlet.

The female Cape Eagle Owl, a creature of awesome beauty and power.

PLATE 21

The sleeping seven-week-old owlet reveals its pink eyelids, a characteristic feature of the species.

The female Giant Eagle Owl with her three-week-old chick; she was photographed with a remotely operated camera positioned near the nest (p. 138).

Portrait of a young Giant Eagle Owl.

Typical Pel's Fishing Owl habitat in the Okavango Delta near Shakawe (p. 149).

A dropped feather provides an exciting clue to the presence of a Pel's Fishing Owl.

This Pel's Fishing Owl at Shakawe was roosting in deep shade; it was my first proper view of this elusive species (p. 149).

A Pel's Fishing Owl with characteristic white shoulder patches; it had occupied the same territory for at least eight years (p. 151).

After six months of preparation Tim Liversedge obtained this picture of a Pel's Fishing Owl with a Tiger Fish (p. 145).

A young Pel's Fishing Owl just out of the nest, photographed by Tim Liversedge.

The tranquil beauty of an Okavango sunset when Pel's Fishing Owls emerge to hunt.

1: *Barn Owl*

The Barn Owl is the most widely distributed land bird in the world and thirty-five races (or sub-species) are recognised. Its scientific name *Tyto alba* is derived from Greek *tuto* (night owl) and Latin *alba* (white). The nominate race (the one that corresponds to the original description and type locality of the species) is *Tyto alba alba* of Britain and western Europe. However, the race that is the subject of this chapter is *Tyto alba affinis* (*affinis*, closely related to) found in Africa south of the Sahara. Interestingly, the African Barn Owl was introduced to the Seychelles in 1949 in an attempt to control the rat population; the plan misfired, the owls preying mainly on birds, in particular the White Tern, one of the most delicate and delightful of seabirds. This ranks as yet another sorry example of what happens when introductions are made without considering the wider implications—the Barn Owl in the Seychelles now has a price on its head.

Wherever it occurs the Barn Owl has figured prominently in folklore and superstitious beliefs. In Britain it is often called the Screech Owl, or White Owl, two names which indicate that its voice and ghostly colour are largely responsible for its earlier unfavourable reputation. Additionally, there have been reliable reports in Britain of phosphorescent 'ghost' owls. This occasional phenomenon is apparently caused by contact with luminous bacteria or fungi on the decaying wood of an owl's roost hole. To see one of these luminous owls as it flies a buoyant but erratic course in search of prey must indeed be an unnerving experience!

My first experience of the Barn Owl in the wild coincided appropriately with a study of *Macbeth* in the classroom. I was just 14 at the time, so it was only later that I came fully to appreciate the skill and impact of the introduction of the Barn Owl into the early scenes. That master of suspense, the late Alfred Hitchcock, could not have done it better. Having fired the unwilling Macbeth to kill his king, Lady Macbeth waits tensely for the outcome. Suddenly a Barn Owl shrieks.

> *Hark!—Peace!*
> *It was the owl that shriek'd, the fatal bellman,*
> *Which gives the stern'st good-night.*

A 'good-night' indeed! For Duncan the good-night of death. One can imagine her tension, even though she tries to rationalise the 'night-shriek'. It should be mentioned that in early performances of *Macbeth* the eerie shriek would be imitated, greatly adding impact to the scene.

Soon afterwards Macbeth enters.

> *I have done the deed.—Dids't thou not hear a noise?*

to which she replies:

> *I heard the owl scream and the crickets cry.*

A further reference to an owl occurs when Ross speaks to an old man outside the castle about the various unnatural events on the night of Duncan's murder.

> *A falcon, towering in her pride of place,*
> *Was by a mousing owl hawk'd at and kill'd.*

This is indeed so unnatural that it eclipses anything the old man can remember. Not only that, it subtly symbolises Duncan the falcon being struck down at the height of his career (he has just won a major battle) by Macbeth operating like an owl. Thus it was not without cause that

> *. . . the obscure bird*
> *Clamour'd the livelong night . . .*

There are other references to owls in Macbeth, but these are sufficient to illustrate the Barn Owl as traditionally a bird of darkness and ill-omen.

During one of my regular week-end bird-nesting outings at this time I found my first Barn Owl's nest in the Cape Town suburb of Constantia, considerably more rural in the 1950s than it is now. While I was inspecting a Hamerkop's nest in the main fork of a large oak tree, a Barn Owl flew out. After some difficulty I managed to extricate the three nestlings and pose them on top of the nest for my first owl photograph. Despite the nostalgic appeal of this early effort, it is of poor quality and I refrain from publishing it. Little did I realise then that the marvels of electronic flash would soon make photography in that dark situation a simple matter. The young owls were undoubtedly the ugliest and most remarkable nestlings I had yet seen. Although still mainly downy, they were beginning to develop their feathers, and the characteristic heart-shaped frame of the facial disc was the most prominent feature. In it were set the rather small dark-brown eyes and the disproportionately large bill—the term 'hatchet-faced' must surely have been coined by someone who had just seen a young Barn Owl? Later, once fully feathered, the Barn Owl is altogether more attractive, as the descriptive Afrikaans name *Nonnetjie-uil* (little nun owl) indicates. After I had ringed them the three owlets were carefully replaced and left in peace.

My second nesting Barn Owl was also in a Hamerkop's nest, this one situated on the ledge of a disused quarry about twenty kilometres from Cape Town. A parent flew from the nest, but to my surprise the nest contained two

Portrait of a captive Barn Owl.

dead nestlings, one of which had been half eaten. It was difficult to imagine that the chicks had died of starvation, for the nest contained several prey items, most of them fairly fresh: a Yellow Canary, a golden mole, a mouse and four gerbils. What had happened? I could only conclude that the owl had killed her own chicks (unlikely) or that they had died from some unknown cause and she had started to eat one, not distinguishing it from prey. Many years later, in Rhodesia, I was to observe other cases of apparent 'cannibalism' and obtain a better insight into the phenomenon. Barn Owls were rare round Cape Town, so I was never able to find a site suitable for photography. Indeed, it was not until I went to teach in Rhodesia that I really came to learn something about them.

On 25 August 1961, the Viscount lined up to land at Bulawayo airport. Jenny sat with our year-old son on her lap and we peered out at the expanse of featureless brown bush below us. A few hours earlier we had left a verdant Cape Town sparkling with spring flowers, and we wondered what we had come to. It was to take us a while yet to make the transition from a winter-rainfall area and adjust to the different pattern of the seasons. We were met by the headmaster, Dougal Turner, and he drove us out to Falcon College which was situated near the small village of Essexvale (now Esigodini), fifty-six kilometres from Bulawayo. Apart from an impressive range of hills before descending into the flat Essexvale valley, the surrounding bushveld seemed as monotonous on the ground as it had from the air. Little did I realise then that I was to contract 'bushveld fever' and remain addicted to this environment. As we turned into Falcon College there was a startling transformation; in the midst of the brown bushveld there appeared what can only be described as an oasis, the playing-fields as green as any we had left in Cape Town.

The reason was soon apparent. The school had been founded in 1954 on the site of the abandoned 'Bushtick' gold mine, where there was an inexhaustible supply of water in the flooded shafts. Once we had settled into our brand-new house, around which we could lay out as large a garden as we wished, I took stock of my surroundings. Beyond the sprawling school village with its avenues of flamboyants and jacarandas, soon to bloom magnificently in the intense October heat, lay three large mine dumps. Farther off in the hazy distance ran a line of hills, the Mulungwanes (Ndebele for 'knuckles'). It was in these hills that I studied many of the eagles that later became the subject of the book *Eagle Days*.

Soon after my arrival the third term started. I took charge of the Natural History Society, which had been functioning without a master in charge for some while; it was soon apparent that Falcon boys were a tough, resourceful and independent breed. With their guidance I was quickly introduced to my surroundings, my newly acquired Land Rover facilitating access to more distant and inaccessible parts. However, the nearby mine dumps provided the focus for much of our attention. Since the closure of the mine many years before, they had been heavily eroded and there were numerous miniature canyons, up to nine metres deep in places. In the sheer walls White-fronted Bee-eaters had excavated their nest burrows and there were several large colonies. They began breeding in September, and by October most nests had chicks.

Dependent on the bee-eaters for nest holes were the Horus Swifts. They usually arrived in September, sometimes earlier, and departed during May. They are assumed to migrate to warmer low-lying areas during winter. Being unable to excavate their own nest tunnels they utilised the excess nest-holes of the bee-eaters (which quite often abandoned old colonies and established new ones) or took over from the bee-eaters in November, once they had finished breeding. Thus quite a workable Box and Cox situation prevailed. Ringing of the Horus Swifts had begun two years before my arrival, the birds being captured in mist nets. After some thought we introduced a new technique. We went to the colonies at night and threw a large tarpaulin over the holes from above; at the bottom of the fissure two catchers would hold the canvas tight while others went beneath to fill their laundry bags with trapped swifts that had flown out. It was not infrequent for us to capture over a hundred birds in a couple of hours, which was more than sufficient if each one had to be ringed, weighed and measured. When there was sufficient moonlight they would be released that night (swifts can see well in poor light) or the following morning if it was very dark.

What were the results of all this effort? In terms of long-distance recoveries negligible, but the chance of a swift being found dead is minimal. We did have one recovery from sixty kilometres away of one of our birds ringed as a full-grown nestling eighteen months before. It was caught at another breeding colony, thus suggesting that young swifts do not necessarily return to their natal colonies to breed. Far more rewarding were the annual recaptures, and as the years progressed these became more exciting. It also indicated that our nocturnal raids were not harmful—not only did the birds survive, but they also returned to the same colonies, although there were occasional exceptions. Eventually our oldest swift was thirteen years old, and I recall the respect with which we handled it. I lost contact after that, but probably many of the swifts I ringed up until 1973 are still flying about. One researcher in Switzerland was recapturing his European Swifts twenty-five years after first ringing them.

Another inhabitant of the mine dumps was the Barn Owl, whose eerie calls were often heard while we were catching swifts. The numerous fissures with crevices in their sides provided a perfect roosting and breeding habitat for the owls. Indeed the whole area was ideal, with its many mine shafts as well. Often in the Mulungwane hills we would flush Barn Owls from inspection pits hewn out by early prospectors. Each of the mine dumps had its own population of owls, but on one we located five occupied nests in a distance of a hundred metres along one side, as well as two others elsewhere. Other owls were also flushed on this dump but their nests could not be found.

All the nests except one were unsuitable for photography, but we checked them each year for breeding, and ringed those chicks we could reach. One particular nest could be reached only by suspending the skinniest and smallest member of the Natural History Society upside down by his ankles over the edge of a fissure; this site was named 'Hallamore's Hole' in his honour. From the thirty-five young ringed we had two recoveries. One was found dead seven years later in Essexvale village ten kilometres away; the other was also recovered dead fifty kilometres away at Fort Rixon two years after being ringed.

An interesting aspect for me was the timing of the breeding season. In the south-west Cape eggs were laid in spring and early summer from August to December, while in Rhodesia, a summer-rainfall area, they were laid mainly from February to May. This was linked to the growth of grass cover after the rains and an increase in the rodent population. In 1967 there was an exceptional breeding season, and most of the nine nests we watched on the dumps contained eight or nine eggs. Several of these pairs raised seven or eight nestlings in a single brood. Elsewhere at this time exceptionally large clutches of twelve eggs were found. The rodent most important in this chain of events was the Multimammate Mouse, a prolific breeder as its name suggests. At the time the Medical Officer of Health was interviewed on television and several articles appeared in the *Bulawayo Chronicle*; all were agreed that it was the worst rodent population explosion in Matabeleland in living memory. At night it was impossible to drive without running over scampering mice.

At this time Viv Wilson of the Bulawayo Museum made a study which dramatically illustrated the link between the rodent population explosion and the productivity of a pair of Barn Owls nesting in a hole in a baobab tree some 220 kilometres from Bulawayo. During the course of other research work he made regular observations at this nest and produced some fascinating results. In an eleven-month period from January to December of 1967 his pair raised four consecutive broods of nine, seven, eight and eight young, a remarkable total of thirty-two young. By way of contrast it is rare for more than four young to be raised in a brood in Britain, and second broods are exceptional, but in this latter respect one must bear in mind the different climatic conditions. On two occasions Wilson found that the first eggs of the next clutch were laid while there were still large young in the nest. It is difficult to imagine the female incubating amongst her importunate brood, so one can only surmise that the eggs were either not incubated initially or that they received partial incubation from the warmth of the young remaining in the nest. As all eggs in each brood hatched, it is clear that the female's haste to lay her next clutch had no detrimental effect. It was also noted in one brood that some of the young left the nest when approximately forty-five days old, earlier than the normal nestling period of between fifty and fifty-five days. Their rapid development was presumably linked to the superabundant food supply. One can only assume that this abundance also enabled them to become rapidly independent, and that they caught their first prey well under the normal period of about a month.

On twelve occasions Wilson made observations from a convenient hiding-place in bushes near the base of the baobab. These watches were always between 6 and 8.30 p.m. On the first evening nothing happened until 6.30 p.m., when the first parent returned with a rodent, followed shortly afterwards by its mate also carrying prey. During seventeen minutes twenty-four rodents were delivered, an average of 3,4 for each of the seven nestlings. Thereafter the owls ceased feeding, although one bird perched in the tree with a rodent which it dropped to the ground. No further visits were made by the time he left at 8.30 p.m., the chicks being obviously satiated. On another occasion he recorded thirty-one rodents delivered to a brood of eight young during his watch. The lowest evening total brought during observations when there were young in the nest was sixteen. When the female was incubating eggs, the male brought her between three and six mice in an evening. These feeding rates eclipse any made in Britain, where the Barn Owl is by no means a slothful bird.

In order to assess the abundance of prey Wilson marked out two parallel transects four hundred metres from the nest. Each was a hundred metres long and twenty metres wide. After each evening watch at the nest he would walk slowly along the two transects flashing a powerful torch from side to side and counting the rodents. On the evening when twenty-four rodents were brought to the nest in seventeen minutes, he counted 138 and 110 rodents in his first and second transects respectively. The transect counts established that rodent numbers remained at a high level and began to drop off only in October.

In addition, some 680 pellets were collected. From these only two rodent species were recovered: 242 Multimammate Mice and 32 Bushveld Gerbils. Clearly the owls were feeding on the most abundant available prey, or as the noted British ornithologist Dr C. B. Ticehurst wisely remarked in a paper published in 1935 on Barn Owl food, 'Opportunity makes the meal.' It is perhaps worth observing here that it is often stated in the defence of birds of prey that they 'control' population explosions. From Wilson's observations it is clear that no such control was possible, indeed on several occasions he saw the owls drop uneaten mice from their perches.

What becomes of all the young owls produced from large clutches and multiple broods in a year like 1967? The answer is that most of them probably die once the abundant food supply disappears. Indeed there was evidence of increased Barn Owl mortality, for example many dead juvenile birds were brought into the Bulawayo Museum at this stage. It is probable also that a number of inexperienced juveniles fall prey to other raptors, like the Tawny Eagle, African Hawk Eagle, Wahlberg's Eagle, Cape Eagle Owl and Giant Eagle Owl, which have all been recorded as predators of the Barn Owl.

At Essexvale it was interesting to note that in 1968 I could find no evidence at all of Barn Owls breeding in the mine dumps. My first thought was that non-breeding was related to the bumper crop of young in 1967, the owls resting on their laurels so to speak. However, it seemed unlikely that they would refrain from breeding if conditions were suitable, or more explicitly if there was an adequate food supply. I decided to relate the two breeding seasons to rainfall.

Summer rainfall in Rhodesia is effectively from October to April, with December, January and February usually the peak months. However, as there had been some rain in September 1967 (21 mm) I included September in both years. In 1967 the September to April rainfall at Essexvale was 738 mm while in 1968 it was 395 mm. The difference was more in distribution than in the total, with 560 mm falling during December, January and February 1967 and 179 mm during the same period in 1968. Additionally, in February 1967, an exceptional 266 mm was recorded. There seems little doubt that just as the good rains of 1967 were responsible for the rodent population explosion, the relatively poor rains in 1968 were at least partly responsible for lack of breeding that year, caused by a cyclic crash in rodent numbers.

I mentioned earlier that one of the nests on the mine dumps was suitable for photography. There was a small shelf barely large enough for my hide six metres from the nest, just within the maximum distance at which my flash could operate. Assisted by Douglas, who combined his gardening activities with ornithology, I set up the hide at 4.30 p.m. When photographing owls it is always wise to be settled and ready well before sunset. We then marked with pegs my route from the hide to the path along the side of the dump; despite the full moon that night I had no wish to plunge to the bottom of one of the many deep fissures. Shortly after 5 p.m. Douglas left me. After carefully checking my focus on the entrance of the nest hole, my aperture setting and my flash position, I settled down as comfortably as possible to wait. It was early winter, so darkness (and the cold) set in rapidly. In the fading light a massed flight of White-fronted Bee-eaters tumbled about like autumnal

Douglas beside the hide at the Barn Owl's nest in the mine dumps.

leaves before retiring to their roost holes for the night. A Familiar Chat, in my experience one of the last birds to retire to roost, hovered in front of my flash head and emitted a series of ratchet-like alarm notes. The three young owls that had maintained a consistent snoring commentary from their nest hole in daylight now fell silent. The silence was eerie, and one thought of Macbeth's words as he invoked darkness to fall before the murder of Banquo:

> *... Light thickens; and the crow*
> *Makes wing to th' rooky wood:*
> *Good things of day begin to droop and drowse;*
> *Whiles night's black agents to their preys do rouse.*

It is a time when, against my better judgement, I have often felt the hairs on my neck prickle. To compound the effect, the rising moon fell on the eroded buttresses of the fissure, and little imagination was required to see faces, which changed as the moon rose higher. Several skulls were thus modelled, and once a perfect profile of Egypt's President Nasser. Those who consider my imagination too fertile could perhaps examine more closely the picture showing the hide—and that in *daylight*.

Suddenly my concentration was sharpened to the purpose of my vigil by a tremulous shriek from a buttress above the hide. It was so unexpected that I started involuntarily, but fortunately did not knock the tripod. Once the adrenalin had settled, I peered cautiously through the peep-hole, but no sign of the owl. Craning forward for long periods makes for a painful neck, but I did not dare take my eye off the hole. Time passed. It was so still that I could hear grains of sand trickling down the small cracks in the buttress behind me. Then, suddenly and soundlessly, the owl perched at the entrance of the nest. As it turned to peer at the hide, I could see its white face quite clearly. I pressed the cable release, and was then dazzled for fifteen seconds by the resultant blinding flash. In this time the owl entered the hole to visit its chicks. After another two visits to the nest, when the parent perched in an identical position, I decided that it was time to pack up.

I emerged from the hide with a hat pulled down over my eyes; Barn Owls are not supposed to attack, but I was taking no chances, and I was well aware that Eric Hosking, the doyen of owl photographers, had lost his eye to a Tawny Owl. As I followed the line of pegs, the owl circled above me emitting an angry double-noted screech, casting a moving circular shadow round me as I went. The mine dumps were flooded with moonlight, so different from the harsh glare of daylight, and had a majestic beauty. It was so bright that I walked back to my Land Rover 800 metres away without the aid of a torch.

Next day, as soon as I had finished teaching, I developed the negatives. To my delight my first exposure had caught the owl perfectly posed, and was the best picture of the evening. It was my first picture of an owl at its nest at night, and although I was later to improve on it I have always been particularly fond of this portrait. I could appreciate the thrill Eric Hosking must have had way back in 1936 (the year I was born) when he used magnesium bulbs, only just produced, to photograph a Barn Owl at an attractive site in an oak-tree. The resultant portrait of the parent with a rat in its bill is the first of an owl taken with flashlight, and it remains one of the best. Unlike mine, his has been reproduced some 1 000 times!

My next experiences with Barn Owls were in 1970 at Shangani, where my close friend Dave Tredgold had recently taken over as manager of the Meikles cattle ranch. He had previously been my 'neighbour' on Essexvale Ranch on the far side of the Mulungwanes, where I had studied Bateleurs and other birds of prey. Dave was a fluent Ndebele linguist and an outstanding naturalist, particularly where trees and their uses were concerned. Such knowledge as I managed to acquire of the confusing variety of Rhodesian trees I owed to him, and he never lost patience when I asked for the identification of the same species for the umpteenth time. In return I was able to teach him something about birds, but not much.

At the headquarters of the Meikles ranch there were numerous empty outbuildings, barns and silos, leftovers from the time when the emphasis had been on crop and dairy production. These derelict buildings provided an ideal habi-

The Barn Owl at its nest in the mine dumps—my first picture of an owl at night.

tat for numerous Barn Owls; during March I found four nests quite easily and knew the location of several others in inaccessible situations in the high roofs of barns and silos. One nest was at the bottom of a corrugated-iron water tank stored in an outbuilding. When I peered into the dark depths, I saw that the owl was crouched there with her brood. The whole floor of the tank was carpeted with pellets, testifying to its long use. I withdrew cautiously and ran to fetch Dave. We returned with a powerful torch and my camera and flash. Looking in we saw that the owl was still there, so while Dave shone the torch I was able to focus, set the correct aperture for flash, and record the scene.

A Barn Owl with its brood at the bottom of a disused water tank.

A brood of Barn Owls in the corner of a loft.

Another nest was in the corner of a huge loft above the abandoned dairy. Entering through a trapdoor, I saw the six downy chicks surrounded by a mass of pellets. They appeared thoroughly uncomfortable as I approached to photograph them and flattened themselves as much as possible into the corner. They had no choice but to pose for a portrait, which they did with considerable taste, to achieve the effect of one of those early group photographs where the participants all manage to look in different directions. I then

The nest of a Barn Owl at the bottom of a pit.

moved on to the next nest I had found at the bottom of a pit which had once been used for servicing vehicles. This was obviously a new site because there were only a few fragmented pellets surrounding the six eggs. When I next visited this nest at 5 p.m. on 11 April, there were two recently hatched chicks, and a third egg was pipping. The following day at midday there were three chicks, two weighing 21 g each and the smallest 14 g. It was interesting that two young had hatched together and a third the next day, indicating that the first egg was probably not incubated the day it was laid and that the first three eggs had been laid at daily intervals. I mention this because textbooks occasionally labour the point that Barn Owls lay their eggs at long intervals so that the last-laid egg is fresh when the oldest chick is ready to leave the nest. In my experience this has never been the case. However, the nest in the pit did illustrate the variability of Barn Owl breeding behaviour, because laying on consecutive days would appear to be infrequent. Rapid laying would seem to be linked to an abundant food supply because of the energy required by the female to produce each egg. In this regard it is of interest that in his study Viv Wilson also records eggs being laid at daily intervals.

The fourth nest was the one I selected for photography. It was situated at ground level in the narrow space where the wall of a silo joined another wall. I placed a hide in position about three metres away and left it there so that the owls could get used to it. On the evening selected for photography the female remained brooding her five chicks while I set up everything in readiness from within the hide. Dave left me, and when the female relaxed I took her portrait. It looked as if things were going to be simple, but I reckoned without the sensitivity of the male. The acuteness of the Barn Owl's hearing is now well known, but the brilliant pioneer study was that of Dr Roger Payne at the Laboratory of Ornithology at Cornell University, the preliminary results of which were published in their journal *The Living Bird* in 1962.

A Barn Owl with her brood in an abandoned silo.

The study was a detailed and complex one, but in essence he established that captive Barn Owls in a special light-tight room he constructed were able to catch mice in total darkness, as long as there were leaves on the floor to produce a rustling sound when the mice ran over them. He found that the owls could locate prey with an error of less than one degree in both vertical and horizontal planes. The external ears of the Barn Owl are situated asymmetrically behind the facial disc, which helps to pick up sound like a reflector. It is this asymmetry which enables the ears to be highly directional at high frequencies because the sound travels along different paths; by moving its head the owl is able to concentrate the frequencies to a maximum and locate the exact position of its prey. Using infra-red techniques, Dr Payne was also able to photograph the owls catching mice in total darkness. The photographs show how the two feet are spread out side by side just before impact. By placing a microphone beneath a piece of paper he induced an owl to leave its talon prints when it attacked the sound. The approximately rectangular spread of the two feet measured 12 by 6 cm. Most fascinating of all, however, was the finding that not only could the owl locate its prey, but also it angled its approach so that the long axis of its killing 'rectangle' ran along the length of the mouse's body, not across it, to achieve a maximum chance of contact.

Pondering this information I sat dead still, so still that a mouse began to chew my shoelaces, which were of doubtful nutritional value. I sat thus for two hours while the female remained crouched over her chicks. Above me in rafters I heard occasional soft, twittering calls from the male, but he never visited the nest. Clearly he was somehow aware of my presence, so I had no choice but to leave the hide and allow him to bring in prey.

In April 1970 we moved into our new home in Burnside, a suburb about eight kilometres from the centre of Bulawayo. I had decided to 'retire' and follow my photographic and ornithological interests on a full-time basis. The move was not made without deep consideration for I had been happy at Falcon College, but I needed more time for writing and research, as well as travelling. However, I kept in close touch with the school and the Natural History Society in particular. I also continued my long-term study of the Essexvale eagles, the results of which became more interesting with the passage of years.

Our house stood in large grounds, and my son was able to keep a horse in a paddock at the bottom of the garden. Of course this was soon severely over-grazed, but it created a habitat for a pair of Crowned Plovers which nested there. As I had done at Falcon College, I soon had nest-boxes distributed round the garden, or logs attached to trees for barbets to nest in. I was particularly pleased when a pair of Scimitarbill Woodhoopoes took over the box near my study window. This enabled me to continue a project started at

Falcon College; to my shame it remains unpublished, but it is probably one of the most detailed studies I have made of any bird. Other birds nesting in the various 'artificial' sites dotted round the garden included Black-collared Barbet, Crested Barbet, African Hoopoe and Lilac-breasted Roller, all of which I was able to study closely.

My new life continued pleasantly and productively; the Bulawayo Museum was a short drive away, where the talented and helpful staff could answer my queries or identify prey remains, while the Matopos hills, one of the richest raptor habitats in the world, were half an hour's drive away.

Then, in 1974, birdlife in the garden took on a new dimension when Barn Owls bred for the first time in a nest-box I had put up for them. For some months I had been aware of 'night-shrieks' in the garden, so early in the year I placed a nest-box on the platform of our six-metre-high water tower. The box measured 80 cm in length, 40 cm in width and 30 cm in height; it had an entrance at one end and the lid could be removed to facilitate nest inspection.

During February and the beginning of March the calling in the garden intensified. This is perhaps a suitable place to discuss the voice of the Barn Owl, which has a complex and varied vocabulary. Researchers in Britain have distinguished seventeen 'sound signals', two of which, bill-snapping (or tongue-clicking depending on one's interpretation) and wing-clapping, are non-vocal. The call most often heard is a drawn-out tremulous screech—*schrrreeeee*—an eerie sound and undoubtedly what Lady Macbeth heard from her 'fatal bell-man'. It serves a variety of functions: for territorial advertisement, courtship and as a contact call. In alarm, for example when the nest is inspected, a high-pitched screech but without the tremulous intonation is used; in anger it is more of an explosive scream, a call that I was to hear often. My favourite call is the soft twittering used for 'conversational' contact by the pair; it is the only one that can be described as at all melodious. In contrast is the snoring noise, of different intensities depending on circumstances. At normal intensity it serves as contact between the pair, particularly during courtship, and as a begging call by the female and young when hungry. In the latter context it has a characteristic wheezy sound. It is emitted at high intensity in threat by the young and has a hissing quality that rises to a crescendo; some have likened it to a nest of angry bees and if heard coming from a dark nest hole it certainly has an intimidating effect. Small chicks make a chittering begging call later replaced by the snoring wheeze. This account is very much a summary of the main calls that most observers would hear: the more complex variations require considerable skill to interpret.

When I inspected the nest-box on 12 March for the first time I found about a dozen pellets lying in the back corner. Rather than risk a desertion I desisted

A Barn Owl brood being weighed.

from further visits until 27 April, when I was delighted to find six eggs and a two-day-old chick. Now I was faced with a dilemma: should I make only occasional visits or risk regular inspections? Although there had been a number of detailed studies on the food of the Barn Owl in southern Africa, that of Vernon (1972) being particularly notable, very little was known of its home life. I decided initially to weigh the owlets and photograph their development. My visits were always in the evening, so that the female could return rapidly in the dusk. I would lower the chicks in a black bag to Douglas, then take them to my study for weighing. He would always wait at the bottom of the ladder because once when I removed the chicks in his absence the female returned to the nest in the few minutes I was away and was momentarily upset by their disappearance. The male was never found to roost in the box at any stage and I was unable to find where he spent the day.

A newly hatched Barn Owl is not a thing of beauty. The pink skin is sparsely covered with white down and it is pot-bellied and megacephalic; its eyes are tightly closed and the long white bill appears disproportionately large. The first noticeable difference is that the eyes are weakly open to slits by the age of nine days; they are fully open by two weeks. By this time the down coat is much thicker, so that the owlet has a woolly appearance. At the age of three weeks the facial disc is distinct and first quills appear on the wings. At a month old the facial disc is feathered and wing and tail feathers break rapidly from their quills. A week later the contour feathers emerge through the down and cover the body by seven weeks except for the abdomen.

Initially the owlet is weak and helpless and is brooded most of the time by the female, who is a devoted parent. I have never watched a small blind chick being fed, but the method described by others is for the female to straddle the owlet from the rear and dangle a small strip of meat so that it touches the bristles at the base of its bill, upon which the chick gapes and swallows the meat. The method is apparently similar for all owls, and I have watched and photographed a Cape Eagle Owl feeding in this manner. The female stimulates the young to beg by calling softly to them and they respond with their begging call. At the age of two weeks the owlets are able to raise their heads and shuffle about; a week later they can stand and swallow small rodents whole. From five weeks co-ordination develops rapidly and, if space in the nest permits, they will exercise their wings and jump about. This is not conducive to sleep if the owls are nesting in one's roof, and thoroughly unnerving for anyone who is unaware that the things going bump in the night are merely cavorting adolescent Barn Owls. Undoubtedly many a 'poltergeist' can be traced to nesting owls.

From the age of about a month the nestlings have a remarkable reaction to danger. They spread their wings, hunch forward, rock from side to side by alternately shifting their weight from one foot to the other, and weave their heads about in circular fashion while staring at the intruder. At intervals the head is completely lowered (so that the back of the head faces the danger) and shaken violently from side to side. It appears exactly as if the performer is about to be violently sick, but suddenly it faces the intruder again and resumes its circular weaving. Cornered adults will also display in similar fashion. It has been suggested that the disappearance and sudden reappearance of the facial disc have an intimidating function; certainly the behaviour must have evolved so that it has survival value, despite the temporary vulnerability of the owl when it hangs its head down. If one attempts to handle nestlings at this age, they will go over on their backs and strike out with their talons: they should be handled with care once this stage is reached, as I have learnt from experience.

Let us return to the nestlings on the tower. I weighed them each day until the oldest was eleven days and the fourth and youngest (three eggs failed to hatch) a day old; thereafter weighings were at irregular intervals. The results are tabulated in Appendix 1. It is interesting to see how chicks three and four caught up in weight to their older siblings, the progress of chick four being particularly rapid. At the age of thirty-six days it had overtaken chicks three and two and was 5 g less than chick one, ten days its senior, with nine days to go before it left the nest. However, it must be borne in mind that the older chicks had already reached their maximum weight, indeed they would be losing weight prior to their first flight. Nevertheless, it is clear that as long as there is sufficient food small chicks are not at a disadvantage. When the smallest chick was a week old I found six uneaten mice in the nest.

Once the oldest chick was two weeks old I began the construction of a hide on the water tower. A perch in the form of a stump was placed near the nest entrance, on which I hoped the owls would pose. The majority of Barn Owl pictures have been taken at nest sites in buildings and, while authentic, they are not particularly aesthetic. I hoped to achieve a portrait free of rafters and brick walls and record the full beauty of the owl against the backdrop of night. The hide was built in careful stages: first a framework on a floor was attached somewhat precariously on the corner of the tower three metres from the perch, then one side was covered with hessian, then the roof, then the remaining sides, and lastly the front. At each stage I checked that the owls accepted the additions, which they did without any sign of alarm.

My first photographic session was on 20 May, my birthday, and I hoped that the owls would give me the ultimate present, their portraits. The young ranged in age from fourteen to twenty-four days and the female was already helping the male to catch prey at this stage. Everything was ready at 5.30 p.m. and soon the cold night air of winter settled in. I could not but think of Keats's lines:

> St. Agnes' Eve—Ah, bitter chill it was!
> The owl, for all his feathers, was a-cold. . . .

Well, I didn't know about the owl, but I was extremely chilled, despite a Second World War fur-lined flying jacket; somehow the cold permeated my nether regions and I was most uncomfortable. Soon all discomfort was forgotten when at 5.50 p.m. the female landed on the perch and posed beautifully. I was able to take several pictures before she flew off. She returned a number of times, enabling me to change magazines on the Hasselblad to secure her picture both in black-and-white and in colour. I heard soft snoring contact calls between her and the male and hoped that he would land on the perch with a mouse in his bill. When he did arrive at 6.30 p.m. he flew directly to the box, scarcely pausing at the entrance. Excited snoring calls from the chicks greeted his arrival, then a few moments later he left. I was fetched from the hide by Jenny at 8.30 p.m., after several more visits by the presumed male, who flew straight in each time. It was difficult to be sure in the dark who was bringing prey, but I gained the impression that the male was doing most of the feeding.

View of the hide, nest-box and perch on the water tower in my garden.

The Barn Owl posed perfectly for its portrait against the backdrop of night.

First thing next morning I developed the black-and-white negatives, and the pictures were all I had hoped for. Two days later I sat in the hide for an hour from six to seven during which time there were three visits with prey. Both birds ignored the perch and flew in directly, so I was lucky to have already obtained the pictures I wanted. This time both owls were too confiding, unlike at Shangani.

The first nestling left the nest during the night when it was fifty-five days old, the second two days later aged fifty-four days. The following morning there were three young in the nest, and either the first or second chick had returned. The situation where two young remained in the nest at night while one returned to roost during the day continued for two days, when two flew out one evening and only the youngest was left. One young returned to join it each day to roost, but there was no way of knowing if it was the same one each time. Eventually all young were out of the box a week after the first chick flew, the smallest chick making its first flight after fifty-three days in the nest. A single young returned to roost in the nest for a further five days, but thereafter the cupboard was bare.

After the nest had been finally deserted by the young owls on 3 July, I removed the lid of the box and photographed the mass of pellets carpeting the whole floor. Then I removed all the pellets except for a few in the corner where the eggs had been laid.

The purpose of removing the pellets was to attempt a calculation of the total food consumed during the incubation period (when the male feeds the female on the nest and she rarely leaves except briefly each evening) and the nestling period. Also included would be a number of pellets regurgitated in the box before incubation, during the courtship stage when the female was becoming broody. These early pellets served an important function because they broke down to form a bed for the eggs on the bare floor of the nest-box; on one subsequent occasion I noted that they had been deliberately scraped together, the closest a Barn Owl comes to making a nest. With the owls breeding on my 'doorstep' I was in an ideal, possibly unique, position to calculate the food consumed during the nesting period.

The problem was how to make the calculation. Others had established that it was not sufficient to break up the pellets, remove the skulls, identify the prey species and then calculate from known weights of these species. This method made no allowance for the considerable variation between young and adult animals. I decided that if I knew what percentage a completely dry pellet was of the original meal, then I could calculate from this. As Barn Owl pellets are very compact and dry slowly, it was essential to achieve complete desiccation if the results were to be of any value.

In preparation for this I had been making tests on a captive Barn Owl. At

Fresh Barn Owl eggs in the nest-box in my garden.

At the end of the breeding cycle the whole floor of the nest-box is carpeted with pellets.

Falcon, and now at Burnside, I had constructed aviaries to accommodate the many injured birds and other unsolicited avian 'gifts' that were constantly being brought to me. One inevitably achieves a certain reputation as a 'Bird-man', which has its advantages and disadvantages in more or less equal parts. On the credit side many interesting species are brought in, and I was able to study and photograph a number of owls in captivity to supplement those observed in the wild.

(Amongst the most delightful inmates of my large aviary in Burnside, apart from owls, were the 'Pollywenkas'. These were young Meyer's Parrots whose nest tree had been chopped down before their presence was discovered. They were brought to me for rearing, one of them with a broken bill requiring particularly careful attention. They became the most entertaining and affectionate pets, flying down to settle on my shoulders and nibbling my ears as soon as I entered the aviary. They had acquired their unusual composite name from the fact that the children called them the Pollies while Douglas used the Ndebele name for parrot *iWenka*. The solution was to combine the two. I kept them for two years and then released them in the garden, where their diabolical shrieks continued for many months until they eventually moved away.)

The disadvantages of receiving birds are considerable. As soon as a new bird comes in it needs to be fed. Birds of prey were reasonably easy because we could trap mice in the garden or feed them meat if the rodent supply dwindled, but insectivorous species required grasshoppers. In summer there was a plentiful supply, but in winter Douglas often had to hunt for several hours before filling a jam jar. Several Lilac-breasted Rollers, which have a propensity for colliding with cars, were brought in. They are voracious birds, but as ungrateful as they are beautiful; each time they were fed a grasshopper they would swallow it then attempt to peck their benefactor.

On twelve occasions the captive Barn Owl referred to previously was fed a single rodent in the evening, normally between seven and nine o'clock. The meal was weighed, and next morning, usually twelve or thirteen hours later, a pellet was regurgitated. Once it was brought up after ten hours, and twice after eighteen hours. Other researchers have shown that a Barn Owl requires a minimum of six and a half hours before a pellet can be formed. The fresh wet pellets were weighed and I found that they averaged 16,3 per cent of the original meal. However, several months later, once completely desiccated, they averaged 8,3 per cent (or half the wet weight) of the original meal. The main limitation of my simple experiment was the small sample size, but pellets from ten weighed meals given to a White-faced Owl gave a fairly similar result, an average of 15,1 per cent wet weight and 7,2 per cent dry. Thus it seemed that my Barn Owl results could be used as a fair indication of the weight of the total original prey. A constant factor seems to be that completely dry pellets are half the weight of freshly regurgitated wet ones and later I found that a few weighed meals fed to a Pearl-spotted Owl confirmed this.

After several months, once the mass of pellets had dried out completely, they weighed 2,8 kg. If this represented 8,3 per cent, then the original weight of food consumed during the first brood was just under 34 kg (or 75 lb). Once the second brood of five young was raised I again weighed the dry pellets and achieved exactly the same result.

I asked my friend Hans Grobler at the Bulawayo Museum if he would analyse the pellets for me, an exacting task which he undertook with characteristic generosity. The results are presented in Appendix 2 and show an interesting shift of emphasis between the first and second broods. The number of shrews recovered from the pellets of the second brood was almost double that of the first, as was also the case with the Angoni Vlei Rats, while the total of forty-one of Multimammate Mice rose to a hundred and five for the second brood. Conversely, the number of gerbils was under half that of the first brood. It revealed clearly the validity of the maxim that 'opportunity makes the meal'. Also, during the period 22 May to 21 June, while the young of the first brood were still in the box, five mousetraps were set in the garden each evening. We trapped three shrews, five Red Veld Rats and forty-one Multimammate Mice. The Barn Owls were clearly harvesting a far wider spectrum of prey than our traps, which meant that the use of traps, at least of the mousetrap variety, was not a reliable method of sampling the whole rodent population.

My account of the Barn Owls on the water tower has jumped ahead in time, but it will be remembered that the young owls of the first brood had left the nest on 3 July. I suspected that another clutch was imminent, so kept a careful check on the nest. On 13 July I found the first egg of the new clutch in the nest and numbered it, as I did all subsequent eggs, in order to establish the exact incubation period. I found that eggs were laid at intervals of either two or three days. Interestingly, although incubation commenced with the laying of the first egg, the incubation period of the first egg was thirty-two days, of the second thirty-one days, and of the remaining three thirty days. Why the eggs should have had a differential rate of incubation I cannot say.

After hatching, the female roosted with her brood until the oldest was a month old, then she left them alone. I discovered that the smallest chick had apparently died at some time between the age of nineteen and twenty-seven days old. It had been completely eaten except for the head and one leg. One can only assume that the female had fed its remains to her brood, but the possibility exists that the other chicks may have killed and eaten it. There is an authentic record in Britain where a fifty-day-old nestling was killed and eaten by its two older siblings. The incident is all the more unusual because it was fully grown by that stage. Conversely, there is a remarkable case, also in Britain, where the youngest of a brood of five was regularly fed by the oldest two owlets—when they left the nest chicks three and four took over the task! The only similar instance to my knowledge occurred in a Black-shouldered Kite's nest in Cape Town, where the oldest nestling fed its two younger siblings.

When the young ranged in age from forty-two to thirty-six days I ringed them. I also marked their bills with small blobs of green, red, blue and yellow paint to be able to distinguish them. The experiment was only partially suc-cessful because the paint wore off quite rapidly. Chick two, one day younger than chick one, left first after fifty-five days in the nest, but it returned the same evening after flying about rather shakily for a while. It then remained in the nest both day and night until three evenings later when it left the box on the occasion of the maiden flight of chick one. Chick two did not return again, but chick one roosted with the remaining two young. The following evening all three left the nest. At this stage the paint on their bills began to come off, but three unidentified young roosted in the nest for a further two days, then only two. The pattern is fairly similar to the first brood, with the young deserting the nest about a week after they could all fly.

In strong contrast to the first brood, which moved off farther afield within a couple of weeks of leaving the nest, the second brood remained in the gar-den for six weeks before moving away. It was impossible not to be aware of their presence because of their vociferous begging sessions at dusk each eve-ning. There was an interesting sequel to the story of the second brood when almost exactly four years later one of the original young was found dead about twenty kilometres away.

The following year at the end of February I found the first fresh pellets in the nest-box, and thereafter further pellets, or fresh rodents brought by the male as part of courtship. The first egg was laid on 16 March and subsequent eggs at two-day intervals until there were eight eggs; the ninth egg was laid after a three-day gap. I was able to establish once that an egg was laid at night, thus confirming two such records by Viv Wilson at his productive nest. All the eggs were numbered as I hoped to confirm the incubation period and see whether the differential pattern applied again. However, my efforts were to be thwarted by a chain of misfortune. Without dwelling on the details, I be-gan to find that eggs were inexplicably crushed or had disappeared. One egg was infertile. Eventually two chicks hatched from the three remaining eggs. Then, shortly after this, a swarm of bees took up residence inside the box. With the help of an apiarist the swarm was removed, but in the process the older of the two owlets was stung on the leg. Its leg became badly swollen, so it was named Oedipus, its sibling Minimus. I weighed the two chicks from time to time and, although Oedipus was older by four days, it showed little gain in weight and was rapidly overtaken by Minimus. Eventually Oedipus died and was later found partially eaten; this confirmed that adult Barn Owls do not kill their young but treat them as food once dead.

An interesting development was that one of the owls began to attack me when I visited the nest in the evenings. The attacks were accompanied by a shrill scream and sometimes bill-snapping, as well as a loud 'klonk' as it struck me. The reason for the last sound was that I always wore a white fibre-glass helmet for protection once the attacks started. It made a perfect target for the owl, and the force with which its talons struck the helmet left me in no doubt that serious injury would have been inflicted had I been unprotected. This attacking behaviour was unusual, and the monograph on the British Barn Owl states, 'There are few, if any, genuine records of Barn Owls attacking Man. . . .' Perhaps it was a case of familiarity breeding contempt—a similar situation occurred in the Matopos, where after many years of study Val Gargett found that one of her pairs of Black Eagles began to swoop menacingly at her, behaviour quite uncharacteristic of the species.

The single nestling was the only survivor of the original large clutch. Fortunately it did not remain solitary for long because I was brought a brood of six Barn Owls that had been removed during construction work at a building site. Two weeks later I was brought two more half-grown young from another source. Thus the owls had nine young to rear, which would have been the situation had all their eggs hatched. They accepted their mysteriously expanding brood with equanimity and reared them all, which was a relief for me and Douglas, who would have been hard pressed to catch enough mice for them had it fallen to us to raise them. Most of them dispersed from the garden after about a month, but one was still heard soliciting for food for a further two weeks.

Just at the time that the young were due to leave the nest another swarm of bees entered the box, undoubtedly attracted by the smell of the previous one. Four young left the nest the evening the bees arrived, but the others remained and were apparently not attacked as they all flew successfully. Once all the young had left, the bees were removed and I took the box down. I had found that the owls did not use the nest as roost when not breeding, so it was safe to keep the box in storage meanwhile. It was replaced early in February the following year (1976), after being washed with a strong solution of carbolic; this proved effective and the bees never returned.

The 1976 season was to be a disaster. The usual signs of residence were noted at the beginning of March and the first egg was laid on 10 April. Eventually a clutch of five eggs was laid at three-day intervals, except for one two-day gap. I wondered why the laying interval varied between different clutches; possibly it was related to food supply, or was characteristic of different females, for I had no way of knowing if this year's female was different from the one that laid at two-day intervals the previous year. The chronicle of dented, crushed or disappearing eggs was similar to 1975 except that the last remaining egg was deserted after heavy unseasonal rain at the beginning of May.

In 1977 I replaced the renovated box on 15 January and three days later a single moulted feather revealed that the owls had inspected their nest. However, the first egg was not laid until 25 March. This time there was a two-day interval between the eggs, except for one three-day gap. I weighed a few fresh eggs to supplement those weighed the previous season; seven eggs ranged from 16 g to 20,5 g, averaging 19,1 g. The female always returned immediately I climbed down from the nest. To my consternation the unsuccessful pattern of the previous year was repeated and no eggs hatched. I decided to intervene and removed one day-old chick from another nest I had found. This was successfully raised and flew after fifty days, shorter than usual, and possibly because of the individual attention it received from two parents. It roosted initially on the low branch of a tree, and when I approached for a photograph it elongated its body so that it resembled an emaciated totem-pole. When this attempt to resemble a vertical branch failed to deceive me it dropped its head and started its weaving display, which I was also able to photograph. The young owl remained in the garden for a month, then moved away. It was my last season with the owls, so I was pleased that they had at least reared something, even if only because of my intervention.

The nest from which I had removed the chick was situated in the roof of a derelict house about fifteen kilometres from my home. Douglas and I built a hide in the roof by utilising the existing rafters as a framework. It was finished in careful stages which the owls accepted. My aim was to obtain a picture showing the whole 'nest' of pellets with the owl bringing in a mouse.

After leaving the completed hide in position for several days, I made my first attempt to obtain photographs. When Douglas had disappeared through the trapdoor to wait outside I settled down to await developments. At dusk I heard the familiar twittering call, and then the soft thump of feet landing on a rafter. For what seemed an age the various 'noises-off' continued, but there was no sign of the owl at the nest. The young maintained a steady snoring begging call as they waited for something to happen. And then, almost soundlessly, the owl was beside the young. I could not make out its position clearly, but decided to risk an exposure. In the stillness the shutter of the Hasselblad sounded like the report of a noon-day gun. The owl was gone, and by the time Douglas came for me an hour later there had been no further visits. We packed up and left the owls to feed their young. Next morning I developed

A young Barn Owl elongates its body in an attempt to avoid detection . . .

. . . when this fails it commences its weaving display.

A Barn Owl brings a mouse to its brood in the roof of a derelict house.

the film for the single valuable exposure; to my intense relief I had captured the whole scene exactly as I had hoped.

Ten days later I made a second attempt, but this time there were no visits at all. As had happened at Shangani, the owls somehow knew I was there, however still I sat. The hide was undoubtedly accepted, the rapid growth of the chicks in the interim testified to that, but once I was inside it that was a different matter. I began to think that owls must have X-ray eyes in addition to their many other faculties. One possibility I considered was that the periodic whine of the electronic flash as it maintained its charge was responsible, but to switch it on just when the owl arrived would produce a loud click (to an owl) which might scare it.

At least I had obtained the one picture I wanted, so the effort was not wasted. It was my last experience with Barn Owls in Rhodesia, for we left a few months later to settle in Cape Town. Now my story has turned full circle, and I rarely see one these days, but the memories of the many hours spent studying the fatal bellman remain.

2: Grass Owl

In contrast to the Barn Owl, the Grass Owl is localised and rather rare in southern Africa. Its habitat is mostly moist open grassland, and thus its distribution is confined to the eastern half of the sub-continent; some dubious records from northern Namibia have recently been convincingly rejected. Because of its specialised requirements the Grass Owl has suffered from loss of habitat and is declining in some areas.

Although there are very occasional records from the south-west Cape, I never saw a Grass Owl in the years I lived in Cape Town before moving to Rhodesia, nor had I seen it elsewhere in South Africa. Thus it was not until March 1974 that I saw my first one in an area of grassland on the outskirts of Salisbury (now Harare) while bird-watching with my friend Alex Masterson, an expert on grassland birds, particularly skulking species like crakes and flufftails. As we progressed through an area of waist-high grass an owl flew up; I just had time to get it in my binoculars as it flew off with its long legs dangling before dropping back into cover. My brief glimpse was sufficient to note the diagnostic features, the white facial disc and underparts contrasting with the almost blackish upperparts. It could not be confused with a Barn Owl, even if one were to occur in such unlikely habitat, because of its distinctive two-tone coloration; the Barn Owl is altogether paler above with delicate buff and grey markings. The more likely confusion would be with the Marsh Owl, but that species shows no marked contrast between the dull brownish upper and underparts, is longer-winged and has pale windows near the wingtips. Alex also pointed out behavioural differences; the Grass Owl flies off with legs dangling and drops quickly back into cover, while the Marsh Owl tucks its feet under its tail and flies round for some while to inspect the intruder.

The thrill of sighting my first Grass Owl was capped a short while later when we found a nest containing a single egg. The 'nest' was a flattened pad of dry grass in a hollow in the rank grass. Alex indicated two further compartments connected by tunnels at the back of the nest; these are characteristic of the Grass Owl and are not found in Marsh Owl nests. These 'spare rooms' serve as funk-holes for the young, but they are also used by the adults for

A view of Grass Owl habitat: Alex Masterson looks down into the nest.

A Grass Owl's nest showing the tunnel at the back.

roosting purposes prior to breeding.

Although the Grass and Barn Owls are closely related and both belong to the family Tytonidae, they occupy quite different habitats. Ecologically it is with the Marsh Owl that the Grass Owl is most closely linked, and they occur and breed in the same areas. It would seem that the larger feet (and perhaps longer legs?) enable the Grass Owl to capture bigger prey, but it eats much the same food as the Marsh Owl, and further investigation of eating habits would prove rewarding. Perhaps it is more the hunting *methods* that separate them, the Marsh Owl quartering the ground on longer transects, settling occasionally and pouncing more often, while the Grass Owl seems to be more purposeful and selective, covering less ground and settling more frequently.

The prey of the Grass Owl is largely rodents, especially vlei rats; it also catches birds mostly varying in size from small passerines to doves, but an Ethiopian Snipe and a Black Crake have been recorded. Frogs are rarely caught, despite their availability, so the owls obviously make no particular effort to feed on them. Various insects are eaten, particularly termites, but then there are few birds that can resist this delicacy so abundantly available in the rainy season.

In striking contrast to the Barn Owl, and to a lesser extent the Marsh Owl, the Grass Owl is rarely heard; indeed some ornithologists maintained that it was voiceless or mistakenly attributed the calls of the Marsh Owl to it. It does call occasionally, but why it should be so silent remains something of a mystery. A muted version of the Barn Owl screech is emitted, as well as a loud hissing by the female and young when disturbed, described by one observer as sounding like several angry Puffadders. A less intimidating snoring noise is used as a begging call by the young. Thus the little that has been recorded indicates similarities to the Barn Owl, but there is ample scope for investigation of its vocalisations by anyone in a position to find out more.

The breeding season of the Grass Owl is rather clearly defined, and although eggs have been recorded from December to August, the majority of records are of February to April. This relates to rainfall and the growth of rank grass cover. Many areas of grassland are burnt off during the winter months, so are only suitable for nesting once the rains have come. Usually three to five white eggs are laid, although there is one record of a clutch of six. Thus the maximum recorded clutch is half that of the largest Barn Owl clutch, and as a rule it tends to lay fewer eggs. According to the few available observations eggs appear to be laid at two-day intervals. However, unlike the Barn Owl, incubation normally begins once the clutch is nearing completion, so that all the young may hatch within a day or two of each other. Sometimes hatching is more spread out, but usually nestling Grass Owls do not show the range in age found in Barn Owls. The incubation period has not been precisely recorded, but is approximately thirty-two days, and therefore close to that of the Barn Owl.

The dry bushveld of Matabeleland where I lived was unsuitable habitat for Grass Owls, so my chances of getting to know the species at all relied on the help of friends living in the grasslands of the Mashonaland plateau centred on Salisbury. An opportunity to photograph a Grass Owl materialised at the beginning of May 1977 when Stephen Lees of Marandellas (now Marondera) telephoned to say he had two nests, one of which had already been photographed by two local photographers. They had taken pictures when the chicks were small and had even recorded the female eating the eggshell of a newly hatched egg. She had been quite tame and spent most of her time crouched over her young.

It was not possible to leave immediately, but within a few days I set off on the eight-hour drive to Marandellas, arriving in the afternoon. Stephen took me to the nest, showing me the other one on the way. Both were situated in hollows in a mixture of vlei grass and bracken, and each contained two chicks, although there had originally been more young which had unaccountably disappeared. Because of the danger of attracting attention to the nest no hide had been left in place, so I quickly erected my portable hide, set up the camera and flash and asked Stephen to move aside any vegetation obscuring my view. Once everything was ready he left me to wait for sunset.

I took in the scene in front of me in more detail now that everything was in readiness. The two young were twenty-six days old at this stage, and of a

At four weeks old the young Grass Owls resemble well-padded teddybears.

similar size. Their facial discs were the only prominent feature, otherwise they were entirely covered in fine, fluffy, buff-coloured down. At hatching, the down had been white, but from about the age of eighteen days they had acquired a luxuriant second coat which made them look like well-padded teddybears. It was notable that the down, in both texture and colour, served as a very effective camouflage, blending with the surrounding vegetation. Once assured that the disturbance round the nest had ceased, and that the hide presented no threat, the nestlings relaxed. At six o'clock one chick regurgitated a pellet, and ten minutes later the other nestling also produced one. Strangely, there was no sign of either pellet when I visited the nest next morning, so one can only conclude that they had been removed during the night by the adults. Next they attended to excretion, squatting and pushing their downy posteriors with a waggling motion into the surrounding vegetation. This behaviour explained why the nest itself was so clean.

The full moon soon threw enough light on the nest for me to see whether an adult arrived with prey. Apart from occasional wheezy snoring calls from the young I heard nothing, but occasional shadows indicated that the adults were in the vicinity and I glimpsed them a few times through peep-holes in the hide. Despite their tameness when the young were small, it was apparent that they were now uneasy about a new hide. The sun had set well over an hour earlier, and prey should already have been brought. Then, just as I considered packing up, an adult alighted at the nest; when it turned its head I saw the white face clearly and released the shutter. Later, when I developed the

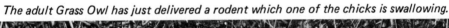

The adult Grass Owl has just delivered a rodent which one of the chicks is swallowing.

film, I found that it had delivered a rodent which one of the chicks was in the process of swallowing. After a further hour when no prey was brought, there was no choice but to dismantle the hide, pack up the photographic equipment and withdraw. One of the adults gave voice to a muted screech when I emerged from the hide, so at least I had personal evidence that the species had a voice!

Over breakfast next morning I asked Stephen if he had any objection to the removal of one chick in order to study its subsequent nestling development in my aviary. It was the only practical way of finding out further details and he readily agreed. I returned to the nest to remove Steve, named after my benefactor, and then travelled on to Salisbury, where Alex Masterson showed me another nest. This one contained a clutch of three eggs, so I was pleased to be able to photograph both the nest and the habitat.

Back in Bulawayo Steve settled into his new surroundings and soon became completely tame. I have treated Steve as masculine for the sake of convenience, but it was quite possible that 'he' may have been a Stephanie. Whenever he defecated, Steve would waggle backwards into the corner of his artificial nest just as he had done in the wild, the only refinement being that he raised his wings at the moment of evacuation. It was an amusing ritual that I never tired of watching. At the age of six weeks Steve appeared almost entirely downy except for the rapid growth of wing feathers. A Barn Owl of similar age would be almost completely feathered. The retention of the buffy downy coat by the nestling Grass Owl is an adaptation with obvious survival value, serving as an effective camouflage in its grassy environment; the Barn Owl nestling in its sheltered nest site can retain its white down colour from birth and can safely feather more rapidly as no camouflage is required. By the time Steve was seven weeks old his upperparts were fully feathered except for some down on top of the head, but his underparts were still entirely downy; it took a further two weeks before this down also disappeared. Steve's facial disc was buff-coloured, a feature common to juvenile Grass Owls. It is assumed that adults have white faces, but breeding birds have sometimes had buff faces. Possibly there is variation in the adult facial coloration, but perhaps those with buff faces are young birds breeding at a year old.

In the wild, young Grass Owls wander off the nest from the age of five weeks, so it is difficult to establish when they first fly. Steve was observed closely in this regard. He began his first vigorous wing exercises at the age of six weeks and could fly short distances at seven weeks.

When Steve was six months old I released him near his nest site during a visit to Marandellas. At this stage his buff-coloured underparts had paled to white on the abdomen, but his buff face still identified him as a juvenile. I had, of course, established that he was capable of catching mice released in the aviary, so there was no doubt that he could fend for himself in the wild. He had provided valuable information, but much still remains to be found out about the biology of the Grass Owl, one of our more elusive species.

3: *Marsh Owl*

I saw my first Marsh Owls while motoring through the Orange Free State at dusk many years ago. I say 'owls' because there seemed to be dozens of them spread over a distance of about two kilometres; many were perched on fence posts while others were quartering low over the grass. Their gregarious behaviour was not unusual, as I later found out, and aggregations of thirty to forty birds may be encountered in a couple of hectares on occasions. Dr John Mendelsohn, who studied Marsh Owls at Settlers, north of Pretoria, tells me that in his experience such concentrations were always associated with termite emergences, and it is interesting to note that they have been observed to hawk termites on the wing. The Marsh Owl is the only species of owl in southern Africa that is gregarious, and this sociability also sometimes applies in the breeding season when nests may be only seventy-five metres apart.

For obvious reasons of habitat, the distribution of the Marsh Owl is similar to that of the Grass Owl, except that its range also extends across into northern Botswana and northern Namibia. Remarkably, there are also isolated records from the Orange River mouth and the Namib desert near Walvis Bay, where there are pockets of suitable habitat.

The Marsh Owl's rather dull coloration serves to accentuate its large dark-brown eyes, set in a facial disc framed in black; it seems to be wearing a permanently surprised expression, as though it has also seen what the butler saw. On its forehead between its eyes there are two small tufts, but these are rarely raised. In flight it is graceful and buoyant, with long wings and diagnostic pale windows near the tips. It is similar in many ways to a harrier, and hunts by quartering low over the grass, occasionally hovering, and dropping suddenly onto prey. Often it hunts during daylight well after sunrise, and again in the late afternoon. At such times it may cover the same ground as African Marsh Harriers, when the similarity of their hunting techniques is evident.

The prey of the Marsh Owl consists of small rodents, birds, insects and occasionally frogs and lizards. In a large sample of prey analysed by Dr Mendelsohn, Multimammate Mice accounted for over 80 per cent of the total. Birds ranging in size from small passerines to doves are caught, but once at

Essexvale I was astonished to find an adult Dabchick in a nest situated two kilometres from the nearest suitable stretch of water. It is the heaviest prey ever recorded for a Marsh Owl, and I am sure it could not have been carried that distance, even if the owl had foraged that far afield, which is unlikely. My guess is that the Dabchick had crash-landed during a night flight, by no means a far-fetched possibility, for once I found a Dabchick at Essexvale scuttling along the ground amongst thorn trees, well away from the nearest water, where it was vulnerable to the first predator that found it. I took it home, filled the bath, and let it recuperate for a few hours before releasing it at the nearest dam.

The Marsh Owl has a number of temporary roosts in its home range, unlike the Grass Owl which usually maintains a single roost where it also breeds. These roosts of the Marsh Owl are merely hollows in the grass where a few pellets may be found. However, it also has the habit of caching prey in times of plenty. When the young leave the nest a number of temporary roosting hollows may be found in a small area, each young owl apparently having its own, and this dispersal of the brood has obvious survival value.

Eggs have been recorded for all months except January, but the majority of nests were found from February to September, with a distinct peak in March and April. This peak is similar to that of the Grass Owl, for the same reasons: good grass cover after the rains, as well as a plentiful food supply. Often nests of both species are found in the same area of grassland or vlei, sometimes only twenty metres apart. The nest is simply a pad of flattened grass in a deep hollow, although sometimes the surrounding grass stems are pulled over to form a canopy. The clutch is two to five eggs, usually three, which take four weeks to hatch.

At the beginning of the breeding season the pair will fly round in wide circles with slow, deliberate wing-beats, uttering a croaking *quark quark-quark-quark* call, an unmelodious sound rather like the quack of a duck. Sometimes the wings are clapped during these nuptial displays. They also indulge in aerial chases and may fly towards each other and touch feet briefly. In areas where there are a number of pairs the dusk may be filled with the harsh calls of displaying owls.

It has been suggested that the names of the Grass Owl and Marsh Owl should be interchanged because the Grass Owl is usually found where it is moist while the Marsh Owl may be found well away from water. I became aware of the validity of this observation, at least in the case of the Marsh Owl, when a nest was found near Falcon College in April 1966. In the preceding five years I had not even seen the species at Essexvale. There had been good rainfalls that year and, while walking in a well-grassed valley amongst the hills, well away from the nearest water, a member of the Natural History

A Marsh Owl's nest in thick grass.

Society had flushed the owl off a nest containing three eggs. Apart from ringing a downy chick found some distance from the nest on a later visit, no observations were obtained that year.

The following year, amongst long grass on a stony hillside, we found another nest, containing four eggs. This time I had the opportunity to make regular visits. Two days after we found the nest the first two eggs hatched. The chicks had pale buff-coloured down and on the tip of their bills was a prominent white egg-tooth. Their eyes were tightly closed and they made a soft chittering begging call. The third chick hatched two days later and the fourth chick three days after the third. Thus the brood consisted of three owlets of much the same size and one markedly smaller. I visited the nest every few days to weigh and measure the nestlings and make a photographic record of their development. The three larger young did not show much difference in their weights, but initially the smallest chick was very much behind. However, by the time the brood ranged in age from fourteen to nine days, the first two each weighed 220 g, chick three 195 g and the smallest 150 g. At this stage I removed one of the two larger young for further study in the aviary because I realised from experience the previous year that the young leave the nest early in the nestling period. My observations established that at the age of a week the down was much thicker, with first quills begin-

Recently hatched Marsh Owl chicks.

A Marsh Owl brood ranging from ten to five days old with prey found in the nest.

ning to break through and the eyes open to slits. At ten days old the eyes were fully open and the facial disc with its black rim was distinct. Feathers were breaking from their quills beneath the down, but the owlet still appeared entirely downy. It is able to stand at this stage and snaps its bill at an intruder. A downy owlet at this age is a captivating creature, its large dark eyes bracketed by the black facial disc so that it wears a woebegone expression. The most striking feature was the rapidity of the nestling development, which explains why the young are able to leave the nest so soon.

During our afternoon visits we always flushed the female from the nest, but once the male also flew up from a roosting hollow five metres away. Normally the female flew around watching us, or perched conspicuously on the tops of bushes, giving vent to the croaking call. When we left the nest she would return as soon as we were about a hundred metres away. However, when the young ranged in age from ten to five days, she gave her first performance of a remarkable distraction display. After circling above us for a while she suddenly plummeted with a crash into the grass and floundered about, exactly as if she had been shot and wounded, then she would fly up again and repeat her act. This distraction behaviour was accompanied by an extraordinary squealing noise rather like that of fighting tomcats. On a subsequent occasion the owl dragged its wings through the grass, just like the 'broken-wing' distraction display of a plover. The whole performance was altogether convincing, and such behaviour would undoubtedly lure a predator away from the nest. At the time I thought that I had discovered something new, but later found that it was regular behaviour, although little had been published about it then.

When the largest chick was eighteen days old I set up a hide near the nest to attempt some photographs. The normal distraction display greeted our arrival, but once everything was in position and my helpers departed, there was silence. As dusk settled in I heard a new call made by one of the adults, a soft snoring *kor*, possibly a contact call. I noticed that the chicks backed into the grass surrounding the nest to defecate, just as the young Grass Owls had done, so that the nest itself was perfectly clean. My captive Marsh Owl in the aviary also backed into a corner whenever it defecated. The chicks now uttered a wheezing *too-eee* call in response to hearing the adults; it carries over a considerable distance but because of its ventriloquial quality is almost impossible to trace back to its source. Certainly the parents can pinpoint the sound so that they are able to locate their chicks once the brood has scattered. Another interesting observation was that the hungry chicks performed a little tap-dance, just as my captive owlet did whenever I approached to feed it.

Once it was dark I decided not to switch on my torch until the chicks gave some indication from their increased calling that an adult was at the nest.

After about an hour I realised that all was silent at the nest and that the *too-eeee* calls seemed to emanate from well beyond it. I decided to shine the torch and found to my disappointment that the nest was empty; the chicks had chosen this very night to decamp! I waited a further hour in the hope that they might return to the nest to be fed, as is the case with nightjar chicks, but my wait was in vain. On leaving the hide I searched around with the torch for the chicks, eventually locating one ten metres away. My presence was greeted with a frantic distraction display by one of the parents, so at least I knew that it was performed both day and night.

The following afternoon when I went to fetch the hide I searched about for the young, eventually finding one thirty metres from the nest with an adult roosting nearby. I found it only because it snapped its bill at me when I nearly stepped on it: its downy camouflage in the grass concealed it perfectly. Thus my only attempt to photograph a Marsh Owl at the nest failed; I realise now that I should have tried earlier in the nestling period before the young were at the wandering stage. As a consolation I was later able to obtain good aviary portraits.

The captive Marsh Owl, in addition to being a delightful pet, yielded valuable information that would have been extremely difficult, if not impossible, to obtain in the wild becasue of the difficulty of locating wandering chicks. It was possible to establish that at the age of a month the back and wings were well feathered, but otherwise it was still entirely downy; at seven weeks, only the forehead and underparts were downy, and it was not until ten weeks old that it was fully feathered. Unfortunately one wing had become dislocated at the carpal joint after an accident, so the owl was never able to fly properly. However, I estimated that it would probably have been able to fly at about six weeks. The owl's first moult commenced when it was eight months old, and over a period of two months it moulted its wing feathers and grew a new tail. A second moult took place at twenty months old, when the wing feathers were replaced more slowly over a five-month period, but the tail feathers were all moulted at the same time and then regrown. Such details would be virtually impossible to obtain in the wild, but one must always avoid the danger of assuming that captive observations necessarily apply in the wild. Because of its injury I could not release the owl, which lived until the fateful day that a Spotted Eagle Owl, lodged temporarily in the aviary, killed it overnight. This was totally unexpected, especially as the killer had been well fed, and cast a gloom over the whole family. At the time of its death the owl was three years and 102 days old.

After the 1967 breeding season, a year of good rains, no further Marsh Owl nests were found at Essexvale, indeed I never saw the species there again. It is probable that it is nomadic, taking advantage of locally suitable conditions, then moving on when these deteriorate. The environs of Falcon College were probably a marginal habitat, hence my surprise when the first nest was found.

Two years later, while I was observing the Barn Owls at Shangani, Dave Tredgold and I flushed two Marsh Owls while out walking in an area of rank grass. Both parents performed the distraction display and, after much searching, we located one chick about three weeks old. During our search we found four hollows, one of which had probably been the nest, and all of which contained dove feathers.

When I had moved to Bulawayo I was brought two 'orphan' Marsh Owls and recognised them by their characteristic wheezing calls even before I opened the box. As it was not possible to find out where they came from, there was no choice but to rear them. They reinforced memories of my first Marsh Owl with their affectionate natures, pre-prandial tap-dance, and the habit while small of sleeping in a prone position with their legs stuck out straight behind them. They made delightful pets and posed for their portraits once fully feathered. However, it was not my practice to keep birds captive unless injured or the subject of study, so as soon as they were able to kill mice in the aviary I released them, not without regret, at Shangani.

4: *Wood Owl*

The Wood Owl is more often heard than seen. Its cryptic coloration and habit of roosting in dark thickets render it easy to overlook unless discovered by small birds which then collect to scold it. The late Charles Astley Maberly, one of our finest wildlife artists, described it as 'the owl with the lovely voice'. Its hooting call is what is traditionally expected of an owl, whereas very few African owls actually hoot. The Wood Owl is the ecological counterpart in Africa of the Tawny Owl of Europe, the species responsible for the loss of Eric Hosking's eye, as well as the subject of Shakespeare's only cheerful reference to an owl—in the song in the last scene of *Love's Labour's Lost*:

> *Then nightly sings the staring owl,*
> *Tu-who;*
> *Tu-whit, tu-who, a merry note . . .*

The call of the Wood Owl is indeed a 'merry note' that merits description. At dusk one hears a high-pitched *eee-yow* emitted by the female, to which the male replies with a low, gruff *hoo* or a bubbling *hoo-hoo, hu, hu, hu, hu, hu,* the last five syllables delivered unevenly with a syncopated rhythm. The female also makes this call, so that the evening may be punctuated with hoots. Various African languages have onomatopoeic versions of the voice of this owl, the Zulu '*Weh, mameh*' (Oh, my mother!) being most often quoted in textbooks.

I saw my first Wood Owl very early one morning in March 1951 as I was climbing Table Mountain via Skeleton Gorge. Perched over the forested path were three owls in a group, presumably still to retire to a less conspicuous position to roost. They were confiding, as is characteristic of the species, and permitted me to look my fill. The most notable feature was their eyes, large, liquid and dark, like those that poets enthuse about when writing of their mistresses. I was also able to note the yellow bill and feet, barred underparts and white spotting on the upperparts, a pattern of markings perfectly suited to concealment in the dappled light of a forest. I was later to deduce that the threesome probably comprised the parents and a young owl, for young may remain with their parents for up to four months after leaving the nest. Skele-

Portrait of a Wood Owl showing the white spotting on the upperparts.

ton Gorge would have remained memorable for the owls alone, but on a previous occasion it had also been the route from which I had seen my first Black Eagle.

Looking back in my first notebook where I recorded the Skeleton Gorge sighting, I see that I wrote 'three Bush Owls', a name I obtained from my first edition of *The Birds of South Africa* by Austin Roberts. At that time the species was known as the Bush Owl, or Woodford's Owl, the latter name after Colonel E. J. A. Woodford, a professional soldier active early last century. Now the name Wood Owl is current, but Colonel Woodford remains enshrined in the scientific name *Strix woodfordii*.

The habitat of the Wood Owl is by no means confined to forest as many people imagine, although it is the only species of owl in southern Africa found regularly inside true forest. It also occurs in thick coastal bush, well-wooded riverine strips, plantations and wooded suburban gardens. Thus it has a considerable altitudinal range from sea-level to montane forest. It may still be heard in the more wooded suburbs of Cape Town, and a few years ago one was even seen on several occasions in the Public Gardens in Cape Town. Along the Liesbeeck River in Newlands, where I now live, I have heard it calling a number of times, once one roosted for a week in the garden, this within earshot of a busy main road. In keeping with its habitat requirements, the Wood Owl's distribution extends in a crescent from Cape Town up the east coast across into Zimbabwe, northern Botswana and northern Namibia.

The Wood Owl is largely insectivorous, but small birds and rodents, as well as the occasional frog, have been recorded as its prey, while there is also a single observation of a snake being caught. Prey is usually taken by dropping down from a perch, but insects such as termites and moths may be caught in flight, behaviour seen by a friend in the light cast from a farmhouse window. Few pellets seem to be regurgitated, and those that are disintegrate rapidly, so that it is difficult to establish the diet in any detail.

During the six weeks or so before laying, the owls are extremely vocal and no form of nuptial display other than calling has been described. Eggs may be laid from July to October, but there is a distinct September peak, so that the young are reared at the onset of summer when insects are plentiful. One to three eggs are laid, usually two, and clutches of three are rare. The usual nest site is a hole in a tree sufficiently deep to conceal the incubating female; no lining is added, the eggs merely being laid on wood chips or leaves lying in the hole. Occasionally eggs may be laid on the ground at the base of a tree or under a log, at other times in the disused stick nest of a raptor such as an African Goshawk or Black Sparrowhawk. One pair made repeated attempts to breed in the funnel at the top of a drainpipe of an outbuilding before moving to a dovecote in the farmhouse garden. The owls remain attached to a nest site, even after repeated disturbance, and in one harrowing early account egg-collectors shot females at the same nest in two successive years for identification purposes and collected the clutch on six occasions, one of which was a replacement after the first had been taken earlier in the season.

Though it is widespread and relatively common in Africa, the Wood Owl's retiring habits make it difficult to study. It was not until Jo Scott, a farmer's wife, found a nest in her garden, and subsequently others, that any details of its life history were obtained. She lived in an ornithologically fascinating area at Chipinga (now Chipenge) in eastern Rhodesia near the Mozambique border. Not far from their coffee farm on the Busi River was the Chirinda forest centred on the hamlet of Mount Selinda. The famous naturalist Charles Swynnerton had lived there from 1900 to 1919 and made a valuable contribution to ornithological knowledge; a small stone memorial with a plaque stands in the forest in which lives Swynnerton's Robin, an attractive small species with a huge eye, an adaptation to its gloomy surroundings.

Jo Scott first made ornithological headlines when she discovered the nest of a Woolly-necked Stork on the farm in 1970, the first Rhodesian breeding record for this species. She was able to study the storks for several years and contributed a valuable paper on their breeding biology to *Ostrich*, scientific journal of the Southern African Ornithological Society. It was through the Woolly-necked Storks that we first met in 1970, when she generously invited me to see the nest. Thereafter I visited Chipinga several times to watch birds and photograph, even managing to find a number of nests of Swynnerton's Robin in the Chirinda forest. The hospitality of the Scotts, and the rich birdlife of the area, make those times at Chipinga amongst the most enjoyable and interesting I have spent anywhere.

However, it was a Wood Owl's nest that provided the highlight for me. In early October 1971 Jo wrote to say she had found a nest with small chicks which was ideal for photography. Two weeks later, once the chicks were well grown, I drove up to Chipinga. As soon as I arrived Jo took me to see the nest on a nearby farm. It was situated in a hole in the trunk of a tree, the entrance just lower than the top of the river bank two metres away where a hide could be erected. Peering into my first Wood Owl's nest with reverence, I saw two delightful downy young within; they were remarkably docile and after a few half-hearted bill-snaps permitted me to handle them. I placed them on the rim of the nest where they sat watching me with interest while I made preparations to photograph them. Meanwhile, high in the tree above, the female peered down anxiously, uttering a soft, mellow *oop, oop, oop* call of alarm. She made this call, which had not previously been described, whenever the nest was visited day or night, but she never attempted to attack, nor are there any records of Wood Owls doing so. Once we had examined and photo-

View of the Wood Owl's nest on the river bank at Chipinga.

Wood Owl nestlings at three weeks old.

graphed the owlets they were carefully replaced at the bottom of the nest hole.

When Jo first found the nest the chicks were two and four days old, and from observations at this nest and others it was possible for the first time to obtain a picture of nestling development. On hatching, the chick has pink skin sparsely covered with white down; its feet are pink, its bill whitish and the eyes are closed. The first noticeable changes are at ten days old when the down is much thicker, the eyes begin to open and quills with feathers just emerging appear on the wings. At three weeks old, the stage at which I first visited the nest, the nestling has a pattern of barring above and below and is feathering rapidly on the upperparts; its feet and bill are turning yellow. By the time it is a month old it is well feathered above, with wings and tail almost fully grown, although still downy on the head and underparts. The young owl leaves the nest while still partially downy, especially on the head, and takes several weeks to become fully feathered, although it remains distinguishable from the adults by its paler head for some while longer.

The following afternoon I placed the hide and photographic equipment in position. To my knowledge the Wood Owl had been photographed at the nest only once before, by Dr Broekhuysen at Somerset West in the Cape some fifteen years previously. He was able to photograph the chick being fed a platanna, an amphibian once famous for its use in the 'frog test' for pregnancy. I wondered what prey would be brought to the chicks in my nest.

I entered the hide at twenty to six, half an hour before sunset. It was too early to expect the owls because they are strictly nocturnal, but there was much to keep me interested. In nearby trees on the river bank a flock of White-bellied Storks clattered in noisily to roost, flapping about for some considerable time before composing themselves for the night. In the dusk I glimpsed a smooth ripple across the pool behind the nest—it could only have been an otter. Innumerable frogs began to call until the air was filled with their tintinnabulations. Then, once the sun had set, the pulsing lights of fire-flies punctuated the darkness.

From the nest I heard the insistent wheezing *shree, shree, shree* begging calls of the owlets, and when I shone my torch on the nest I saw that they had come up to the entrance and were bobbing their heads about in expecta-tion of a meal. The first visit with food was fifteen minutes after sunset when a parent perched on the rim of the nest hole. When I took a picture the owl flew off, but shortly afterwards another came. Subsequently, by examining photographs, certain differences in plumage and colour established that both parents were feeding. In the half hour after the first visit food was brought rapidly; sometimes only a few minutes elapsed between visits. The feeding rate slowed down in the next half hour, when the adults may have been hunt-ing for themselves, before picking up again with regular feeds until 8.30 p.m. Thereafter visits were infrequent until I left the hide at 10 p.m.

The following evening I observed and photographed again. As the owls were now completely used to the hide and flash, their behaviour was con-sidered quite normal. The first visit was at 6.25 p.m. with some ten visits in the next twenty-five minutes. Then followed the usual lull during which the nestlings took turns to stretch their wings out of the entrance. They were never seen to defecate out of the nest hole, and yet it remained remarkably clean except for some hard white droppings around the perimeter; possibly the diet of insects was the reason for the nest not becoming fouled. Then the feeding rate increased with thirteen visits until the magical hour of 8.30 p.m., after which there were only two further visits before I left just before ten o'clock. In three hours and forty-five minutes since the first visit of the evening there had been close on twenty-five feeds.

Two nights later I made my final watch, this time using the motor-driven body of the Hasselblad to try to obtain some flight photographs. This meant that I had to watch a patch of moonlight on the pool behind the nest and re-lease the shutter as I saw an owl silhouetted against it. A moment's inattention meant a missed picture; how I wished I had had sophisticated equipment so that the owl would fly through a light beam on approaching the nest and take its own picture. Instead I craned forward with my eye at the peep-hole watching for the shadow against the patch of moonlight. Sometimes the owl was too quick for me, but in the end I obtained a number of pictures, only one of which was really successful—it shows the alighting owl with wings back, feet thrown forward and an insect in its bill. My neck was painfully stiff the next day, but the discomfort had been worth it.

Apart from observations on the feeding rate, a few other details of the Wood Owl's life had been gleaned. We knew something of the behaviour of the owlets at night, that both parents fed, and that they brought mostly insects carried in the bill. From my photographs (fourteen showed recognisable food) and careful inspection of the nest immediately after photographic sessions, twenty-one items were recorded: a frog, an unidentified rodent, a king cricket, a hawk moth, a cicada, a cricket, two termites and thirteen unidentified insects. One parent with a yellow-and-red hawk moth in its bill gave me my best picture—it could even be identified for me by Dr Elliot Pinhey, entomologist at the Bulawayo Museum, as *Theretra capensis*.

From our observations at the Chipinga nest Jo and I wrote a paper for *Ostrich*, incorporating also such published information as we could trace. Subsequently Jo continued her study of the life history of Wood Owls, establishing amongst other things that the laying interval is about thirty-six hours, that the incubation period is thirty-one days, that the young leave the nest between thirty and thirty-seven days, before they can fly properly, and that the young remain with their parents for up to four months after leaving the nest. This last piece of information enabled me to deduce, twenty years later, that the threesome I saw in Skeleton Gorge were a family group. Jo Scott's observations on Wood Owls, as well as other species, serve to illustrate the importance of the contribution of ordinary bird-watchers to the advancement of our knowledge.

The Wood Owl perched at the nest entrance.

5: White-faced Owl and African Scops Owl

I saw the White-faced Owl for the first time in June 1951 while on a trip to what was then Southern Rhodesia. We had entered at Beit Bridge on our way to Bulawayo and were motoring north along a 'strip' road, so characteristic of Rhodesia in those days and for many years to come. This form of road, to save on cost, consisted of two narrow tar strips, and required skill and concentration to keep one's wheels on them. The problem arose when a vehicle came in the other direction—how long dare one stay on both strips? It was probably on those harrowing roads that the game of 'chicken' evolved. Fortunately there was not much traffic in those days, but after an hour or so our driver decided that we should take a picnic break under a clump of trees. As soon as we alighted I scanned the branches for birds, as is my habit, and there sat two White-faced Owls!

They were perched beside each other on a branch near a flimsy stick nest which I assumed to be theirs, but on consulting my early edition of Roberts I read that they laid in stick nests of other birds. Many years later I realised that the nest was that of a Grey Loerie, a slight platform of sticks, indeed the one above me was so thin that I could see through it and it contained no eggs, although I have little doubt that the owls were intending to breed in it later.

I have given the impression that I identified the owls easily, but I was 15 at the time and still learning my birds, indeed on this trip as far north as the Victoria Falls, my first across the Limpopo, I saw in excess of a hundred species new to me. My immediate problem was to decide whether they were Scops Owls or White-faced Owls, for both looked very much alike on the colour plate before me, and the Roberts of those days did not give a great deal of help with identification in the text. In size they were closest to the Wood Owls that I had seen for the first time a few months previously, but the measurements given for the Scops Owl indicated that it was markedly smaller. Also, as their name suggests, the White-faced Owls had strikingly white faces boldly bracketed with black, while the Scops Owl has a grey face that does not contrast with the rest of its cryptic coloration. The orange eyes of the

White-faced Owls were particularly noticeable, those of Scops Owls being lemon yellow, but this was a distinction learnt later, for the illustrations were too small to show such details.

On our arrival the owls had stiffened up, elongated their bodies, half closed their eyes and erected their ear tufts. This helped them to look less conspicuous, but, as I was to learn later, White-faced Owls may often roost where they are by no means well concealed, whereas a roosting Scops Owl is almost impossible to detect except by chance. The owls, thinking themselves undetected, remained on their perch while we had our picnic below, giving me ample time to examine them in detail.

Those White-faced Owls had to last me just over twenty years, for I did not see the species again until I settled in what had become simply Rhodesia in the interim. The main reason for this is that the distribution of the White-faced Owl extends northwards of a line from Durban across to the Orange River. It occurs in a variety of woodland habitats but is most common in drier acacia thornveld, occurring for example in the Kalahari, where it may sometimes be seen by searching thorn-trees in the camps of the Kalahari Gemsbok National Park. However, during my trips north from Cape Town in the intervening years, I was never lucky enough to encounter it again. Even when I lived in Rhodesia I did not come across it all that often, seeing only three nests, none of which was convenient for study, although I did photograph at one site. During my years at Essexvale I saw a White-faced Owl once, roosting conspicuously on a slender branch of a syringa early one morning. Had any lived permanently in the school grounds I feel sure I should have heard their characteristic call, a rapidly repeated bubbling hoot *wh-ho-ho-ho-ho-ho-ooo* drawn out at the end.

But for the efforts of two Salisbury schoolboys, C. J. Worden and J. Hall, very little would be known about the biology of the White-faced Owl. They had studied a breeding pair for several years and submitted the results of their research as a project for the 1977 Rhodesian Young Scientists' Exhibition. This exhibition, held alternately in Salisbury and Bulawayo, was an excellent medium for fostering scientific investigation, and in several cases projects started at school were later expanded into the subject of a thesis at university. I was a judge on one occasion in Bulawayo and have seldom spent such a fascinating few days; the ingenuity of some of the young exhibitors was at times amazing. The project of Worden and Hall was later published in *Honeyguide*, magazine of the Rhodesian Ornithological Society, where all could read of their outstanding work. It illustrated yet again the importance of an amateur contribution to our knowledge of a hitherto little-known species.

The White-faced Owl is far more rapacious than its size would suggest, taking much larger prey than the Wood Owl for example. It hunts from a perch from which it pounces on its quarry. Small rodents feature largely in its diet, but it also feeds on arthropods and the occasional bird. In their analysis of prey Worden and Hall found that pellets contained 85 per cent rodents, 10 per cent arthropods and 5 per cent birds. The largest prey they recorded was a Tree Squirrel, but birds the size of a Laughing Dove were also captured, creditable kills for an owl of this size.

Nuptial display consists of the bubbling hoot, and the male may approach the female along a branch while bobbing his head up and down and hooting. He also chases after her if she flies off. Eggs have been recorded from June to November (there is a single February record from Namibia), most frequently from August to October. Laying would appear to be timed before the onset of the main rains so that the incubating owl in its unsheltered nest is not exposed to wet weather, but doubtless other factors also affect the timing of the breeding season. The eggs are usually laid in the stick nests of other birds, quite often the disused nest of a bird of prey, but also in crow and Grey Loerie nests, as well as on the top of the nests of such species as Scaly-feathered Finch, Cape Sparrow, Wattled Starling and Red-billed Buffalo Weaver. In fact almost any nest providing a suitable platform is used, but that of a Grey Loerie is probably the most flimsy chosen. They also breed in an open hole in a tree, or in a hollow where several branches converge. There is no evidence to substantiate the claim of some observers that this owl builds its own nest, a misconception that has undoubtedly arisen because of the insubstantial nests it sometimes chooses.

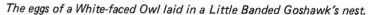

The eggs of a White-faced Owl laid in a Little Banded Goshawk's nest.

Two or three eggs are laid which take thirty days to hatch. The female incubates during the day but Worden and Hall established that the male assists with incubation during the night for periods of about half an hour at a time. This is one of the few instances I know where evidence of incubation by a male owl has been obtained. During daylight the female sits tight, flattening herself on the nest if anyone approaches. Once I climbed to a Little Banded Goshawk's nest in which an owl was incubating and it sat tight until I was almost at the nest. Sometimes she may even remain on the nest and defend herself with her claws.

The newly hatched chick is covered in greyish-white down and at four days old its eyes begin to open. By the age of two weeks it is feathering rapidly and a week later is almost fully feathered, at which stage it begins wing exercises. The young move out onto branches near the nest at the age of about a month, and from one record it seems that they first fly when about five weeks old. Thereafter they remain with their parents for at least two weeks, but the period is probably much longer because detailed observations on the post-nestling period are lacking.

My one opportunity to photograph this species was through the help of my friend Dave Barbour, a forester at Sawmills in teak woodland north-west of Bulawayo on the road to the Victoria Falls. The owls had obligingly chosen to lay in the fork of a teak tree just behind his house. The nest was only three metres above ground and was ideal for a hide, which Dave had placed in position before I arrived. He had already taken some pictures himself at night and warned me to be cautious, the female having raked his scalp and drawn blood. Others have been attacked by White-faced Owls, so it is a species not to be trifled with.

The hide was two metres from the nest, and when we climbed up to install the camera the female flew off. She perched on a branch above the nest and gave vent to a remarkable snarling call; in my notes I likened it to the sound of two fighting tomcats, an alarm call with as much sound and fury as I had heard from any raptor. The nest contained a five-day-old chick and an egg which later proved to be infertile. Soon after Dave left me, the owl returned to brood, settling gently over her chick, which greeted her arrival with a soft chittering call. As darkness fell, the female remained brooding her chick, glaring at the hide whenever the flash went off. After about an hour she made a soft chirruping call and left the nest to collect prey from the male, returning with a gerbil. This she proceeded to tear up, feeding small pieces to the chick. Its appetite was soon satisfied, so she settled once more to brood it, a position she maintained until Dave fetched me from the hide. Once again she greeted the disturbance with her furious snarling call. That brief evening was the limit of my experience with the White-faced Owl at the nest, but it

The female White-faced Owl settles to brood her five-day-old chick.

The female White-faced Owl tears up a gerbil.

is known that the female continues to brood the nestlings until they are about two weeks old, but with some difficulty because of their increasing size and mobility.

Several years after I had photographed at the Sawmills nest a White-faced Owl was brought to me. It was in poor condition and appeared to be blind, its pupils remaining wide open even in daylight. However, as I was not sure whether it had some vision, I made an appointment with Dr Greenwood, a Bulawayo opthalmologist, who showed a great interest in the case. After an exhaustive examination he pronounced the owl totally blind, almost certainly because of a blow on the front of the head in some accident. The appointment overran its time somewhat, so when I left there were several people in the waiting-room. I shall never forget the expressions of disbelief on their faces as I emerged clutching a staring owl under my arm.

In view of its blindness I decided to name the owl Oedipus, and felt rather pleased with the classical touch. However, Jenny objected to this pseudo-erudition and suggested that we call it Love. When I expressed puzzlement and asked why she said, 'Well, Love is blind!' So thereafter the owl was called Love. He (if I may once more attribute sex arbitrarily) lived with us for some two years before dying during a cold spell, possibly from old age. Each evening I would feed the owl, and all that was necessary was for me to touch the bristles at the base of his bill with a mouse, whereupon it was seized, transferred to the feet and torn up. Love was able to find his way around the various perches in the aviary with remarkable skill after a few weeks, and with a regular diet of rodents his emaciated condition soon improved. Sometimes, if something strange startled him, he would emit the snarling alarm call. For a short while Love was joined by a young White-faced Owl brought to me after confiscation by an official of the Department of National Parks (as an honorary officer of the department I had offered to assist in such cases). The young owl differed from Love in its paler, fresher, plumage, greyer coloration on the face and paler orange eyes. Once I was certain that it could catch mice for itself I released it.

If my personal knowledge of the White-faced Owl was limited, then by comparison I knew virtually nothing about the African Scops Owl, and I have never seen an occupied nest. I refer to it as the African Scops Owl to distinguish it from the Eurasian Scops Owl, which some authorities consider to be the same as our species. However, in southern Africa, it is generally considered a distinct species, and it is convenient to treat it as such. For the sake of a less cumbersome text I will refer to it as the Scops Owl, which is what most people call it anyway when they see it in the wild.

Very little indeed is known about the biology of the African Scops Owl because it is difficult to see, and its nest even more so to find. During the day the owl roosts against the trunk of a tree, or next to a snag, where its cryptic markings make it almost impossible to detect except by chance. If it feels threatened it will elongate its body, erect its ear tufts and close its eyes to the merest slits, so that it blends with the bark of the tree or looks like part of the snag next to which it is perched. Except for the nightjars, the Scops Owl has few rivals in the art of concealment. By comparison, as I have indicated, the White-faced Owl hardly gets to first base. Fortunately, the Scops Owl calls regularly each evening at dusk, the male and female answering each other with an insect-like ventriloquial *prrrup* at approximately five-second intervals. It is a call that carries over a considerable distance and, if I am sitting by a campfire, it immediately enhances the whole bushveld atmosphere. Initially, one may not recognise it as an owl at all; Anthony Walker, Rhodesia's expert on recording bird calls, thought it was an insect for several months before someone enlightened him.

The distribution of the Scops Owl is more limited than that of the White-faced Owl and it is absent from the Karoo and the dry western regions. It may be found in any dry woodland habitat, usually where there are larger trees. The first time I saw a Scops Owl was in August 1966 while on a camping trip to the Nata River in the north-east corner of the vast Makgadigadi Pan in Botswana. We were out on the open plain where there were a few rather straggly thorn trees. When we stopped near one of these to identify a lark, I detected a shape amongst the thorns; my delight may be imagined when it turned out to be my first Scops Owl in somewhat atypical habitat. Compared

My first Scops Owl was roosting in a thorn tree.

A Scops Owl roosting against the trunk of a tree is almost invisible (photograph: Alan Weaving).

with my few subsequent views of them, this owl was by no means well concealed, but if one looked away it still took a while to relocate it. I was able
to obtain a picture which shows a great deal of thorn-tree somewhere in
which is perched the owl, but it serves as a reminder of that memorable
occasion.

The Scops Owl lays from September to November, but there are few breeding records. The nest is usually a natural vertical hole in a tree. Two or three
eggs are laid, but the incubation period and other details of breeding biology
are unknown. As far as I know, the Scops Owl has been photographed only
once at the nest, by Alan Weaving in Rhodesia. Unfortunately, his observations were abruptly cut short when a Tree Monitor (or Leguaan) was found
in the hole after eating either the eggs or small chicks. He established that at
dusk the male called from his roost 120 metres from the nest before setting
off to hunt. The male would come to the nest with insects and enter the
hole to feed the female, or she would come up to the rim of the nest to take
food from him. As the female refused to leave the nest when it was inspected,
Alan Weaving could not find out whether the nest contained eggs or small
young. All the prey that he observed brought to the nest, or that he found in
pellets, consisted of insects, thus confirming that the Scops Owl seems to be
entirely insectivorous.

Alan Weaving has generously permitted me to use two of his pictures to
supplement the few that I have. While on a short visit to Maun in quest of
Pel's Fishing Owl in the Okavango Swamps (see chapter 11) I was shown a
roosting Scops Owl which I was able to photograph at close quarters. I took
pictures under natural conditions and with flash; the latter showed the owl
up well but eliminated its subtle camouflage which relied on shadow. On
another occasion while staying near the Kruger National Park we made a tape-
recording of a resident Scops Owl, which responded to its own voice and
came down to a branch over the camp fire, close enough to be photographed
with flash.

The Scops Owl is a prize for anyone who can find its nest and has time to
study it. Meanwhile, for most of us, it remains an enigmatic voice in the
African night.

A Scops Owl emerges from its nest hole at night (photograph: Alan Weaving).

6: *Pearl-spotted Owl*

I was fascinated by the Pearl-spotted Owl long before ever seeing one. One of the most treasured books of my boyhood was a copy of *Birds of the Gauntlet* by H. von Michaëlis, in which he wrote about and illustrated the birds of prey he had kept. I have never seen drawings that can compare with his studies of young raptors at various stages of development, and those of owls were particularly delightful. One species he received from up-country (his home was at Somerset West in the Cape) was a Pearl-spotted Owl which arrived in a small box. On opening it he thought it was empty, until he saw the diminutive owl pressed into one corner attempting to escape detection.

As I lived in Cape Town at the time, there was no chance of seeing this little owl, which is found north of the Orange River in bushveld habitat, especially in acacia woodland. Once I moved to settle in Rhodesia, my chances of seeing it were good, but tantalisingly it still eluded me for several years. I heard it at night on a few occasions while out camping, but somehow I could not manage to see one during the day. I even had my doubts about the authenticity of the call I heard, but friends who knew the sound well assured me that the owl produced it. What strained my credulity was the sheer volume of noise produced by such a small bird, a series of clear, whistling *tiu, tiu, tiu, tiu* . . . notes which began softly and increased gradually in intensity before achieving a penetrating crescendo. Sometimes a second owl would join in antiphonally.

Then came the day when I was walking through a copse of large acacias on Ntabenende farm a few kilometres from Falcon College. Suddenly a small bird flew across an open area between the trees before alighting. From its dipping mode of flight I took it at first for a woodpecker, but somehow it seemed different, so I walked nearer and trained my binoculars on it. What I saw can only be described as heart-stopping: a diminutive, rather long-tailed owl that could have fitted into a tall drinking-glass. Fortunately it showed no fear of me, so I looked my fill and noted all the salient features: a rounded elfin head with large yellow eyes set under white eyebrows that gave it a permanently indignant expression; large feet; boldly streaked underparts; white spots scattered like raindrops on the head, back and long tail. These 'raindrops' give it its name, for they do resemble small pearls, as the specific Latin name *perlatum* (wearing pearls) also indicates.

After watching the owl for some while, a remarkable thing happened. When several small birds gathered to mob it, it turned its head to glare at them, yet there was still a face looking at me! The illusion was caused by two dark patches on the back of the head, each surrounded by white, so that they looked just like two eyes. Another African raptor, the Bat Hawk, has white occipital

A Pearl-spotted Owl showing the false face at the back of the head.

'eye' spots, and when it sleeps its closed eyelids are also white, so that it appears to be looking both ways like the Roman god Janus. The most logical explanation of this interesting phenomenon is that the rear face serves to deter a potential predator, but there may be other interpretations. One wonders also why the Barred Owl, which belongs to the same genus *Glaucidium* as the Pearl-spotted Owl, lacks occipital 'eyes'.

When the owl eventually flew off I distinctly heard a slight whirring noise from the wings, whereas most other owls would have flown soundlessly. This fact clearly indicated that this species does not need to rely on stealth and hearing to catch its prey, indeed it is largely insectivorous and moves about freely during the day, when it will also hunt. However, the large feet suggested that it could be rapacious at times, so it was not surprising to learn that it also caught small birds and mammals, lizards, amphibians and the occasional small snake. One observer witnessed a male Masked Weaver being snatched as it was building its nest, and once I saw one with a freshly caught agama lizard at eleven in the morning. In Botswana it has been seen to catch small insectivo-rous bats in flight as they rose from the water after drinking. The largest kill on record was either a Laughing Dove or Cape Turtle Dove at a water-hole. A friend was breakfasting in the bush one morning when he noticed a dove on the ground about forty metres away across the water. At first he thought it had been struck down and dropped by a Peregrine hunting in the area, but while he was examining the corpse through binoculars two fierce yellow eyes appeared from behind it, and then the rest of the Pearl-spotted Owl—it had been lying on its side clinging tenaciously to its quarry until all movement ceased! The incident illustrates the fearlessness and rapacity of this little owl on occasions. Sometimes it also indulges in piracy; in Kenya one robbed a wood hoopoe several times as it went to its nest with food. Although direct evidence is lacking, it may also prey on the young of hole-nesting species, possibly when prospecting for a nest site itself.

It did not require an extensive examination of the literature to find out how little was known of the breeding biology of the Pearl-spotted Owl. Now that I had seen it, the next step was to find a nest to study. Some idea of the size of the owl may be obtained from the fact that it breeds in the nest holes of woodpeckers and barbets, although natural holes are also sometimes used, as well as in nest-boxes if suitably situated. Eggs are laid from August to October, usually in September or October, and the clutch is two to four eggs. Although nothing was recorded then, it was subsequently established that courtship consists of the female uttering a monotonous ventriloquial *peep* call near the nest, the male sometimes answering her. She calls for about a month prior to laying, and as the *peep* call is repeated at intervals of thirty seconds for long periods it can be tedious indeed. During this nuptial period the male regularly brings prey for her and they mate frequently.

Almost exactly five years after I had seen my first Pearl-spotted Owl I found a nest in the same patch of woodland on Ntabenende farm. I had searched the area in the interim but could not find a nest; then in September 1971 my luck changed and I saw a pair perched near a woodpecker hole. Looking through binoculars I saw a single owl's feather caught on the entrance, so I climbed the ten metres to the nest to inspect its contents. For hole-nesting species I use a light bulb at the end of a flex attached to a small battery and a dentist's mirror for looking in; very few nests fail to reveal their contents using this simple technique. The nest was empty, but while I was inspecting it one of the owls perched a few metres away and uttered a series of sharp *peep, peep, peep* alarm notes, at the same time wagging its tail up and down in agitation. Encouraged by these signs I returned two weeks later and saw the owl peering from the hole on my arrival. It flew out when I climbed the tree, and when I lowered the bulb and looked in I was rewarded by the sight of three white eggs, their pink glow of freshness visible by the light of the bulb. Having at last seen my first occupied nest I left quickly, so that the owl could return to incubate.

Three weeks later I returned to check for hatching. No owl was seen peering from the entrance and when I had almost reached the nest I banged on the trunk to inform the owl of my presence. Nothing happened and I feared the worst. On lowering in the bulb my heart sank because the hole appeared empty with only some débris lying at the bottom; but then the 'débris' moved slightly and I glimpsed two eggs. What I had been looking at was the owl lying in a prone position with its face flat so that the back of its head was uppermost. Subsequently I saw this behaviour several times, and it seems to be a regular reaction to deceive a potential predator, a very effective one, for the owl looks just like débris at the bottom of the hole. A week later the same procedure was repeated, but I was just able to see the edge of an egg when the owl moved slightly.

I estimated that the eggs were due to hatch—as it turned out quite an accurate guess, as the incubation period has subsequently been found to be twenty-nine days. Several days later I returned with Douglas to erect my pylon hide made of lengths of tubular aluminium. We assembled it to a length of ten metres on the ground, but then followed the difficult task of pulling it into a vertical position with ropes. Somehow we managed it and I secured the top end to the tree with a plank as the guy ropes did not give sufficient stability. It served its purpose, but when I sat at the top rather like a fakir on a pole it was with faith rather than certainty that the whole structure would hold together.

The next day Douglas left me in the hide an hour before sunset. The dis-

My first picture of a Pearl-spotted Owl is also my most memorable.

cordant crowing calls of Swainson's Francolins shattered the evening air, followed at dusk by the eerie yelping calls of jackals echoing across the veld. Before entering the hide I had checked the nest and knew the owl to be inside, so when I heard a soft *too-woop* call nearby I assumed it to be the male. Then I heard scrabbling noises in the hole and a face appeared at the entrance and glared indignantly at the lens. I released the shutter and in that moment secured one of the most delightful pictures of my photographic career. As the flash went off, the owl left the nest like a cork out of a pop-gun. Now I heard both *too-woop* and *tee-weep* calls, the latter higher-pitched call that of the female; these soft calls are used by the pair to maintain contact. When the owls had moved some distance away I decided to inspect the nest, a necessity as I had not been able to see the contents because the owl was always in the hole in the prone position during daylight. I crossed the plank from the hide to the main trunk, trying not to think of the drop below, and lowered in the bulb. To my intense disappointment there was a single egg in the nest, the other two eggs having mysteriously disappeared. I then climbed back to the hide before the owls returned to the vicinity and awaited developments. At seven o'clock an owl came to the nest and I took its picture just before it popped back into the hole. After waiting two hours during which there was no activity I left the hide to return to the farmhouse.

The following evening I tried for further pictures, this time hoping to take the owl in colour as it emerged. The previous evening the face had appeared at ten minutes past six, so from six o'clock I kept my eye glued to the peephole, an uncomfortable craned position which causes a painful condition I call 'bird-photographer's neck'. Then at seventeen minutes past six the scrabbling was heard, a face appeared at the hole and I took my picture. The owl returned to incubate after ten minutes and did not emerge again.

By the time I returned to the farmhouse at ten o'clock my hunger was sharpened by the cold night air. My hosts, Douglas and Olive-Mary Robinson, were away for the night, but they had arranged that the cook should leave my supper in the Aga stove. There seemed to be innumerable compartments and I could not find my plate of food, although eventually I located an enamel bowl in a bottom drawer in which there was an appetising stew of some sort. This I consumed with relish while the family Corgi sat and watched me; to my shame I must admit that I was too hungry to share my meal with a dog that appeared so well fed. The next day the Robinsons returned and subsequently asked me why I had not eaten my supper—the cook apparently was quite upset. It transpired that my supper had been in yet another compartment and I had eaten the Corgi's meal prepared for the next day! Douglas Robinson was known in the district for his dry sense of humour, and when I left he said, 'Let us know when you are next coming so that I can order some dog biscuits.'

A Pearl-spotted Owl about to enter its nest hole.

The remaining egg at the Ntabenende nest failed to hatch and it was two years before I was able to study the Pearl-spotted Owl at the nest again. On a visit to Wankie (now Hwange) National Park the Warden of Robins Camp, Cliff Freeman, showed me two nest sites in hollow-log nest-boxes put up in the camp. Both were occupied by owls and only 200 metres apart, one in a tree above the tourist office, the other in Cliff's garden. The one at the office contained three eggs on 17 October, but the next day an egg had inexplicably disappeared. The nest in the garden had two small young and an egg. Interestingly both nests contained a few fresh green leaves, something I had also noted at the Essexvale nest. It could only be that the owls had lined their nests, very unusual behaviour for an owl, but no other observers have seen green leaves in nests.

In the few days I was based at Robins Camp I made daylight observations at both nests and took photographs at night at the nest in Cliff's garden. I established that the incubating female left the nest during the day for short periods and that the male roosted nearby, chasing off any intruding birds; in one instance a Red-billed Hornbill was put to rout. At the nest in the garden the male spent a short spell brooding the small chicks and the unhatched egg, behaviour that indicated that he probably assists during the incubation period. When the egg hatched I was able to weigh the minuscule chick, which tipped the scales at a mere 7 g. Although my observations were limited, at least I knew a bit more about their lives, as well as having taken further pictures at the nest at night.

Not long after returning from Wankie I went to check the nest at Essexvale. The birds had not bred on Ntabenende farm in the original hole the previous year, but when I climbed up to check I found that they had returned and the nest contained three recently hatched chicks, two of them about two days older than the third. It was 10 a.m. and I decided to watch the nest for a while from a vantage point below; eventually I stayed for seven hours enjoying the doings of the owls. While the female was in the nest, the male spent his time resting, chasing off other birds or feeding the female. Species he chased away from near the nest were Kurrichane Thrush, Boubou Shrike, Crested Barbet and Lilac-breasted Roller; he was particularly vigorous in chasing off the barbet and the roller, both hole-nesting species. He fed the female in the nest on three occasions with insects, and she left the nest for an airing six times. Her breaks from the nest lasted for a minute or as long as half an hour, but only once did she return to the nest with an insect. Just before four o'clock she joined the male to feast on emerging winged termites, but neither of them took any back to feed the chicks. The most amusing incident of an interesting day was when the male had just caught a millipede and a bold Kurrichane Thrush attempted unsuccessfully to rob him. The female was out of the nest at the time and the male gave it to her to eat.

I visited the nest subsequently on three occasions but made no long watches. I noted that once the young were feathered they too adopted the same prone position as the female had done when the nest was inspected. One evening I watched for an hour and saw that one owlet came up to the entrance, bobbing its head about in expectation of a meal, but I did not see the adults come to the nest. Only two young were in the nest at this stage, the third having disappeared.

Although I had found out a fair amount about the breeding biology, there were still gaps, which were filled by a friend Warwick Tarboton. He was fortunate to have a nest near his house at Nylsvley in the northern Transvaal which he could visit regularly. One evening, for example, he observed extremely rapid delivery of prey to the large nestlings, twenty-three Harvester Termites, a frog and a toad, in a period of forty minutes. He also recorded details of the development of the nestlings. At ten days old they are covered in greyish-white down and their eyes are still closed. Three days later the eyes open and first feathers are just visible through the down. At seventeen days there is rapid feather growth and at the age of three weeks the nestlings appear fully feathered. At Essexvale I had established that the nestling period was not less than twenty-seven days but Warwick obtained it more accurately as close on thirty-one days. The young leave the nest when their tails are still short and they lack the pearl spots of the adults. They do not return to the nest to roost; otherwise nothing is known of the post-nestling period.

My observations at Essexvale in 1973 proved to be my last. When I returned to the nest in 1974 to check for breeding I found that the hole had been taken over by a swarm of wild bees. However, I had been brought a slightly injured Pearl-spotted Owl which had been living in the aviary for two years; named Pearly by the children, he was a delightful pet. He provided me with wonderful insight into his character, and his behaviour confirmed or supplemented observations of wild birds. His tail wagging, which could be up or down or a more vigorous flick from side to side, was usually indicative of agitation, as I had seen when I climbed up to nests. Once, when I temporarily introduced a young Black-shouldered Kite into the aviary, it landed on a perch beside Pearly. Instead of giving ground as I expected, Pearly faced the kite squarely and glared at it, ducking his body and then bobbing up to his full height with the feathers on the back of his head raised. After a few of these ferocious stares and bobs the kite fled to the other side of the aviary. Nothing I knew could frighten Pearly, and even in the wild a Pearl-spotted Owl will show no fear of a bird many times its size.

Another facet of Pearly's behaviour was his fondness for bathing, and he was frequently seen soaking himself in the plough disc placed in the aviary as a birdbath. If it rained he would spread his wings and tail and shower instead, a charming sight as the raindrops joined those of his plumage. On two occasions Pearly moulted his tail, dropping all the feathers at once, so that he was a rather ludicrous sight. This feature is common to a number of small owls. It has been suggested that because they are mainly insectivorous they do not need their tails to manoeuvre, so it is biologically advantageous to replace the tail quickly rather than extend the moult over several months.

Because he was used to people, Pearly never played possum, as did a stunned Pearl-spotted Owl brought in to the Bulawayo Museum. When it recovered and could fly it would sham death if handled by lying on its back with its eyes closed, but if thrown into the air it would fly normally. This death-shamming behaviour has also been observed in the Barn Owl of Britain as well as the Giant Eagle Owl of Africa.

With a little bit of motivation and effort I had been able to contribute new information on the biology of the Pearl-spotted Owl, but much remains to be learnt. Meanwhile this fearless little owl remains amongst my most treasured memories of the African bushveld—when I hear its clear, whistling call rising to a crescendo, I know that I am back in my spiritual home.

7: *Barred Owl*

The larger Barred Owl has a superficial resemblance to the Pearl-spotted Owl, and they both belong to the same genus *Glaucidium*, but the two are readily distinguishable if a good view is obtained. Perhaps the most striking feature of the Barred Owl is its large 'puffball' head; on its wing it has a bold white bar, far more prominent than that of the Pearl-spotted Owl, and where that species is spotted above the Barred Owl has barring. Ventrally it differs too in having a barred gorget, the rest of the white underparts being boldly blotched.

The distribution of the Barred Owl in southern Africa needs to be considered according to the two races (or subspecies) found in the region. The commonest of the two is *Glaucidium capense ngamiense*, first collected in the Maun region of Botswana. It is widely distributed from the eastern Transvaal northwards to Zimbabwe and in northern Botswana and north-eastern Namibia. The other race *Glaucidium capense capense*, the nominate one, is an enigma. Two specimens were obtained in the eastern Cape Province in the first half of last century, and the species was first named in 1834 by the eminent naturalist Dr Andrew Smith. The eastern Cape race is readily distinguishable from *ngamiense* by its very much darker coloration, narrower barring on the tail and a chevron pattern of spotting instead of barring on top of the head. Having been named and described, the Barred Owl of the eastern Cape 'disappeared' for some 150 years and was thought to be extinct there. Then in 1980 a freshly dead male was picked up in the middle of Kenton-on-Sea and taken to the bird artist Graeme Arnott, who immediately realised the importance of the find. After he had sketched it in detail it was deep-frozen and despatched to a delighted Dr P. A. Clancey at the Durban Museum; he had predicted that it still existed in the eastern Cape as a valid subspecies and had now been vindicated. The story illustrates the elusiveness of owls. (As recently as 1965 a species new to science, the Sokoke Scops Owl, was found in the Sokoke Forest in Kenya, an area by no means remote which had been well investigated by ornithologists.) The nominate race of the Barred Owl has also been recorded at Durban at the turn of the century, collected once and seen twice in Zululand, and recently one was seen in Transkei. Thus in just over 150 years there are apparently only eight records of this elusive owl in southern Africa.

The Barred Owl inhabits woodland, usually where there are larger trees along rivers. Though sometimes overlapping the Pearl-spotted Owl, it is generally found in denser woodland. I have seen the Barred Owl on three occasions, each time in quite thick woodland near water. The first time was on the Chobe River near Kasane in Botswana. I was bird-watching with a friend, who suddenly stopped and pointed ahead, but when I looked into the thick cover I could see nothing. Eventually we realised that I was looking too high and the owl was sitting on a low branch a metre off the ground. Like my first Pearl-spotted Owl it showed no fear and I was able to absorb every detail. It was mid-morning, so it was also an owl active during daylight, when it sometimes captures prey. My second Barred Owl was seen on the Nuanetsi River in the south-eastern Rhodesian lowveld. We were camping on the bank of the river where there were large trees. I became aware of the owl's presence in the late afternoon when I heard a repetitive, mournful *krrooo, krrooo, krrooo* call rather like that of a Cape Turtle Dove. It lacks the vivacity of the Pearl-spotted Owl's crescendo whistle, indeed the owl's whole demeanour is somewhat phlegmatic by comparison, and it rarely wags its tail in excitement. I located the owl high in a tree and when it flew off it had the same dipping woodpecker-like flight as the Pearl-spotted Owl.

The habits of the two owls are very similar. The Barred Owl is also mainly insectivorous, dropping from a perch to catch its prey, but there is little detailed information on its diet, although it has been recorded to catch lizards, a frog and a small bird. While on present evidence the Pearl-spotted Owl is seemingly the more rapacious species, the lack of information on the diet of the Barred Owl precludes such an assumption.

My knowledge of the Barred Owl would have been tenuous, indeed this chapter could not have been written, were it not that my third sighting of the Barred Owl led to the finding of its nest. One of the most active societies at Falcon College was the Exploration Society, whose reports usually took up a quarter of the annual school magazine, not without good reason. The driving force was a mathematics teacher, John Stakesby-Lewis. As a former Queen's Scout he was an excellent organiser, with a gimlet eye for detail. Therefore it was ironical that the heavy truck he hired each year usually broke down in a remote spot and had to be repaired. This was such a regular feature of his expeditions, which also included various four-wheel-drive vehicles, that I came to the conclusion that the truck was chosen *because* it might break down! Certainly, after the first break-down, a cohesive spirit prevailed amongst the schoolboys, who had all been pulled in to assist with mechanical work, changing a burst tyre or just pushing. John believed that mud and grease were great levellers and good for team spirit, or so it seemed.

Once the destination had been reached (and somehow it always was) everyone was detailed to setting up camp. A roster of cooks was posted, two schoolboys each day, and one of their main tasks was to bake bread in a three-legged pot. Usually the bread was delicious, occasionally awful. Another of John's priorities was hygiene, and a team would be appointed to dig a pit latrine immediately on arrival. He also insisted on a toilet-roll holder made from sticks, over which a plastic bag would be slipped. His elaborate waterproof design gave an opportunity for one particular wag amongst the schoolboys to name him 'Sticks-by-Loos'.

The expeditions were by no means just a 'jolly in the bush' and invariably had a clear scientific purpose. To this end we were always accompanied by members of the National Museums staff, usually from Bulawayo, and various collections of insects, birds, amphibians, snakes and plants, would be made, often including very valuable finds. Dr Elliot Pinhey, entomologist at the Bulawayo Museum, invariably stole the limelight, despite his unassuming nature. Rare insects were attracted to him like moths to a candle, if one may be forgiven a somewhat unfortunate comparison.

In 1973 a destination in the Okavango Swamps of Botswana, called Four Rivers Camp, was chosen and I was invited as ornithologist. It was ninety kilometres west of Khwai River Lodge, a well-known luxury camp. On a previous expedition to the Khwai area another schoolboy wag asked John Stakesby–Lewis if he had remembered the playing-cards. When John looked bewildered he replied, 'Well, sir, aren't we going to play bridge on the river Khwai?'

We set off on 1 December for Botswana, the party consisting of thirteen schoolboys and nine leaders or their technical assistants; we even had a doctor with us this time. The first night was spent beside the road just beyond Francistown, and next day we travelled along the northern end of Makgadigadi Pan (where I had seen my first Scops Owl) and on to Maun, focal point for any journey to the Okavango Swamps. That night it rained, a foretaste of several wet nights to come. Next morning we set off for Khwai River Lodge, which was reached without too much difficulty. Then we set off westwards, enjoying the game viewing along the way, tsessebe being particularly plentiful, but we also saw hyaenas and lions. The road deteriorated into a sandy track, and the five-ton truck had to be pushed repeatedly. In the end we were overtaken by darkness and had to camp out in the open beside the truck.

The remaining forty kilometres took us five hours, the heavy truck requiring to be pushed, towed or dug out on some twenty-five occasions. By the end of all that John Stakesby–Lewis had his team spirit (as well as some black looks). Four Rivers Camp was an excellent site under large shady trees with no facilities, which we would not have wanted, and was merely a name on the map where professional hunters occasionally camped.

That evening I heard a Barred Owl calling and saw it perched on a branch just on the edge of our camp. I heard it regularly after that, even during the day, and noted a soft, mellow *twoo, twoo, twoo*, probably a muted variation of the usual *krrooo, krrooo, krrooo* call.

Our days were busy as we explored the area, not without adventure, as two of my schoolboy ornithologists found when they came across a sleeping lioness and lost themselves when making a wide detour to avoid her. Dr Pinhey's adventures were less dramatic, but no less exciting. He obtained another specimen of the dragonfly *Trithemis falconis*, first caught on the 1968 expedition to the Khwai area; it was new to science then and named in honour of Falcon College. On this trip he collected two new species of dragonflies, as well as *Anax bangweulensis*, only known previously from five specimens on Lake Bangweulu in Zambia. Ornithologically we had little chance of discovering anything new, but we made several unsuccessful attempts to collect the rare and elusive Slaty Egret for the Bulawayo Museum. Two of our days were spent on a boat trip from nearby Xugana to Gadikwe lagoon to see the spectacular heronry there. We seemed to travel endlessly between walls of papyrus as we wound our way down the narrow channel. On reaching the lagoon we found that breeding was nearly complete, but we saw some Marabous and Yellow-billed Storks with large young, as well as various other herons and egrets.

We returned to camp to learn that one of the boys on cook duty had seen an owl emerge during the previous afternoon from a hole in a tree just thirty paces from where I had set up my stretcher. While I was chasing all over the swamps for birds, the real prize had been back in camp! The nest was in a natural hole in a tree just under six metres from the ground. When I lowered in the inspection light, it illuminated a Barred Owl which refused to leave or reveal the contents. Although I set a watch on the nest the female did not leave it during the day until the late afternoon three days later. I climbed up to inspect it immediately and at the bottom of the hole was a single owlet, a mixture of down and feathers.

From the few available records the nest seemed typical, a natural hole in a tree. Possibly because it is too large the Barred Owl has not been found breeding in barbet or woodpecker holes, but there are too few records to be conclusive about this. Eggs have been recorded in September and October, and clutches of three have been found. One observer states that he lifted the incubating owl bodily off the eggs to see the contents.

Apart from the description of a few nests and their contents, virtually

The hide at the Barred Owl's nest in the Okavango Swamps: the nest is arrowed.

The Barred Owl about to enter its nest.

nothing was known about the breeding biology of the Barred Owl, so we had an ideal opportunity to learn something new about it. The morning after I first saw the chick we erected the pylon hide two metres from the nest, the female remaining in the hole. At seven o'clock that evening I was installed in the hide. The female had left the nest earlier and did not return until an hour later, when she came to the nest with food which was given to the chick at the entrance. After ten minutes she again returned with food and entered the nest, where she stayed for twelve minutes before emerging. A while later she returned with food and stayed in the hole. I left the hide for a while before resuming observations and at about 10.30 p.m. the male made two quick visits with food which he passed in to the brooding female. When there were no further visits by 11.15 p.m. I went to bed. At 5 a.m. I awoke to watch for any early-morning feeds but there was no activity. I gained the impression that the Barred Owl was more nocturnal at the nest than the Pearl-spotted Owl, but as there was always someone in the camp during the day the owls may have been inhibited from visiting the nest during daylight.

The owl had proved completely tame, so I decided that we would watch the nest the whole night. It was also our last chance as we were leaving the next day. We hung a gas lamp on the hide to illuminate the nest, and the owls ignored it. Three of us watched the nest overnight from 7 p.m. until 5 a.m. the following morning. Again the first visit was not until just after 8 p.m., with a further five feeds in the next hour and a half. Most of the prey was insects, but one small frog was brought. During the remainder of the night feeds were sporadic—only five further visits with no increase in activity towards dawn. Both birds brought food and they communicated with a soft *twoop* call. Although the chick was estimated to be three weeks old at this stage the female still spent long periods brooding it at night; during one spell she spent two hours and twenty minutes in the hole.

We had learnt a little about the Barred Owl's nest life, but not enough. As I sat in the hide that night, I decided to take the owlet with us next morning so as to study its further development, especially as it was an opportunity that would probably never come again. The hole was just big enough to admit my hand, and the owlet snapped indignantly as he was lifted out. I placed him tenderly in a small photographic gadget case, which was to be his home on the journey back to Bulawayo. For the first time I examined Oliver (as he was soon christened) in detail. His upperparts were well feathered but his head and posterior were still downy. His eyes were pale yellow, the bill greenish-white and his tongue and gape black, in contrast to the pink gape of a Pearl-spotted Owl. The last detail may seem rather trivial, but it is best to record such things as one never knows when they might turn out to be significant.

So much for Oliver's external appearance; as a character he was the most

The Barred Owl emerging from its nest.

A portrait of Oliver, the nestling Barred Owl, at about three weeks old.

delightful owl I have ever reared. Like all young owls he was of a confiding nature and soon adopted me as his parent. When I opened the gadget case to feed him he greeted me with a rapidly repeated wheezing *chip, chip, chip* begging call, stretching his neck upwards to double his length, which explained why the adults had not needed to enter the 25-cm-deep nest hole to feed him. When he defecated he pushed his rear end against the side of the 'nest', behaviour apparently characteristic of all hole-nesting owls. As I was driving along I heard vigorous fluttering inside the case on the seat beside me; on opening the lid I found that Oliver was indulging in some wing exercises, despite the enclosed space. When I returned home and he was a little older I observed other mannerisms, like the ecstatic stretch when he extended a leg and a wing simultaneously, at the same time half-closing his eyes. On being offered a grasshopper or similar tasty morsel he would raise it in one foot to his bill just like a parrot with a peanut.

By the time he was a month old Oliver was fully feathered except for a few stray wisps of down on his head and some fluffiness on his abdomen, while his tail was just visible beyond the folded wing tips. He had the basic adult pattern of markings except that the top of his head was spotted, not barred, and the blotching on the underparts was not clearly defined. Oliver had not

Oliver was totally confiding: here he nestles in Dave Tredgold's neck while he is asleep.

yet been put in the aviary and lived in a spacious box where he performed his vigorous wing exercises. His box was usually next to my desk in the study where I could watch him, and he was a constant distraction. Once, on a whim, I dropped in a rolled-up ball of paper, which he immediately attacked and 'killed', rolling onto his side and flapping as he hung on, behaving more like a playful kitten than a bird. Oliver made his first short flight at an estimated age of thirty-three days, a nestling period very similar to that of the Pearl-spotted Owl. The only post-nestling observations on the Barred Owl are from Tanzania, where the young left the nest and hopped from branch to branch before being able to fly two days later. This conformed with Oliver's aerobatics; he too required a few days before he was confident on the wing.

It was not until seven weeks old that Oliver's tail had grown out to its full length. It required a further two weeks before he was fully feathered below with the handsome blotching of the adult. When two months old he made his first attempts at calling, producing a rather broken-voiced mewing note, but it was only at the age of seven months that the first full *krrooo, krrooo, krrooo* was heard, a performance that gave as much pleasure to me as it did to Oliver. A few months later he moulted his tail, dropping all the feathers at once just as Pearly had done.

Oliver at a month old indulging in an 'ecstatic stretch'.

A portrait of Oliver once fully feathered.

Oliver (right) with Pearly the Pearl-spotted Owl to show differences between the two species.

Although Oliver had provided several pieces of valuable information, one could never think of him as a mere subject of study. His affectionate nature endeared him to the whole family and all who met him. Once he could fly he was introduced into the aviary, where, after an initial period of mutual suspicion, he and Pearly became companions. I was able to photograph them on the same perch together, a unique opportunity to illustrate the difference between the two species.

Just under a year after I found him I decided to release Oliver, a difficult decision which caused an outcry from the family. However, he had been able to kill mice for some while and was quite capable of fending for himself. It was not my practice to keep a healthy bird in captivity unnecessarily, and by this time Pearly's slightly damaged wing had mended completely, so I released them together on a wooded hill at Essexvale not far from my first Pearl-spotted Owl's nest. I had heard the *krrooo, krrooo, krrooo* calls of Barred Owls on the hill, but had never been able to locate them. I like to think that when Oliver called of an evening he did not go unanswered.

Oliver tears up a mouse.

8: *Spotted Eagle Owl*

The Spotted Eagle Owl is probably the best known of all our owls, mainly because of its habit of perching on roadside telephone poles or fence posts at dusk. It has a characteristic silhouette with the 'ear' tufts as the most prominent feature. These tufts, of course, have nothing to do with hearing, and their main function seems to be to disrupt the owl's outline and enhance its cryptic pattern when roosting. However, two Norwegian ornithologists have suggested that in Europe the 'ear' tufts (or 'horns') of three species of European owls serve to mimic the facial patterns of potential mammalian predators such as the lynx, pine marten and fox. In 'face to face' encounters they suggest that a specialised aggressive facial expression on the part of the owl may cause its potential 'look-alike' predator to withdraw. The most probable predator of a ground-nesting Spotted Eagle Owl is a Caracal. One wonders whether such a ferocious predator would withdraw, or indeed whether possible mimicry is sufficiently close to support the idea. It is perhaps an aspect that merits investigation in an African context, but it is difficult to see any close parallels between our eared owls and their likely mammalian predators.

During the day the Spotted Eagle Owl lies up in a roost, relying on its cryptic coloration for concealment; it is flushed only by chance, and then it flies off for some distance before settling again. Almost invariably birds gather to mob it, so even when it attempts to hide itself its position is revealed by the alarm calls of the birds following it, thus enabling one to have a good look at the owl and note its main features.

Invariably the ear tufts will be raised to their maximum height as the owl glares with large yellow eyes at its tormentors. The eyes, so vital to its nocturnal way of life, are the most striking feature of this owl, which has a drab but functional grey-brown plumage. The face is bracketed with black, the breast blotched with grey, and the rest of the underparts finely barred grey and white. The upperparts have some randomly distributed white spots that serve to enhance the owl's camouflage, but it is difficult to see why it was ever named 'spotted', as nowhere is spotting a distinguishing feature of its plumage. The only species with which the Spotted Eagle Owl could readily be confused is the Cape Eagle Owl, especially with the rufous plumage form of the Spotted Eagle Owl which occasionally occurs. The distinctions between the two species will be discussed in the next chapter.

The Spotted Eagle Owl is widespread and common, indeed it is a species likely to have been seen by most people even if not aware of its identity. Sadly, all too often, it is seen too late in the headlights of the car before the almost inevitable collision with the dazzled owl. For those who see it in time a valuable life can be spared by hooting and dipping the headlights, but such consideration, or even awareness, is the exception. Thus it is almost impossible to drive along a country road for any distance, especially in the early morning, without seeing a dead owl, sometimes several. One observer in Namibia counted twenty-six dead owls along a 200-kilometre stretch of road. One tries not to think how many die a lingering death beside the road when they are not killed outright. At the World of Birds in Hout Bay near Cape Town there is a large cage filled with Spotted Eagle Owls brought in by sympathetic members of the public: almost all are so badly injured that they can never be released into the wild again. Sometimes a pitiful roadside corpse provides useful miscellaneous information, for example on parasites: once I counted forty-five ticks on the head of an owl, most of them concentrated round the eyes, the base of the bill and the ear openings.

If one drives along country roads at night, as I frequently did when living at Essexvale, it soon becomes apparent that the owls are highly territorial and usually I would see them in the road in the same places whenever I travelled a particular route. There has been much speculation about the reason for owls sitting in roads: one suggestion is that it is for warmth, especially on tar roads on winter evenings, but it is more probable that the owl uses the road like a transect to watch for prey crossing, particularly insects such as beetles. Whatever the reason it is frequently a fatal habit.

At dusk the owl leaves its roost to hunt, usually flying to a favourite prominent perch nearby from which it watches for its prey. Normally it swoops down onto its prey, but sometimes insects are caught on the ground by running after them. In one observation a fruit bat was taken in flight, but such agility is probably exceptional. Another exceptional observation was made by the late Leslie Brown, who drove along beside a foraging Honey Badger in the Kalahari Gemsbok National Park for five hours one afternoon. During its travels the Honey Badger was followed for some distance by a Pale Chanting Goshawk, behaviour that had already been recorded by others, but at one stage a Spotted Eagle Owl left its roost to follow it, flying from tree to tree, over a distance of several hundred metres. This was in broad daylight and is an interesting case of opportunism; the owl, like the goshawk, followed the badger for anything it might disturb.

Small mammals, birds and arthropods are the main food of the Spotted Eagle Owl, but it also preys at times on amphibians, reptiles and occasionally fish. It probably also feeds on carrion in the form of road kills, but direct observation of this is lacking. However, I was told recently of an occasion when two Spotted Eagle Owls, presumed to be a pair, fed one night on freshly dead mullet left lying on the quayside of the harbour at Hermanus in the Cape. Although its diet consists mainly of smaller mammals and birds, as well as a great many insects, this species is capable of some large kills for its size. Avian prey records include a hornbill, pigeons, a sandgrouse, francolins, a Lanner Falcon and a Black-shouldered Kite. It may also possibly prey on other owls because on the wire roof of my aviary in Bulawayo I once found a bunch of soft feathers, clearly shed when a wild Spotted Eagle Owl had attempted to attack either a White-faced Owl or Pearl-spotted Owl which were in captivity then. Larger mammalian prey records include a Night Ape and young hares.

I saw my first Spotted Eagle Owls when I began my secondary schooling at Diocesan College, or Bishops, in Cape Town in 1950. The Bishops owls, which had been in residence for as many years as anyone could remember, roosted in a huge stone pine near Founders House. The daily traffic of pedagogue and pupil below drew as little attention from the owls as the wind sighing through the branches of their ancient pine. However, in the breeding season, this peaceful coexistence was sometimes temporarily disrupted. One became aware in the evenings of increased hooting during the courtship period, the male's *hoo-hoo* being answered by the female's triple hoot *hoo-hoohoo*, the middle *hoo* higher, so that the call had a pleasing cadence. Usually the pair would duet, the female answering her mate immediately, so that it sounded like a single owl hooting.

The owls chose to nest in a hollow filled with pine needles at the junction of the slate roof and the stonework of the Founders clock tower. I remember my envy when a senior member of the school's Ornithological Society took photographs from a nearby study window once the chicks had hatched. He used flash bulbs at night, but only one of his pictures was really successful, showing the owl staring at the camera with a mole in its bill. My photographic career was in its infancy and I lacked both a flashlight and a telephoto lens. All I could do was look again and again at that marvellous portrait and dream of one day emulating it; little did I know then that it would be some thirty years before I was to photograph a Spotted Eagle Owl with a mole in its bill.

A few weeks later there was at least partial compensation for my disappointment at being unable to photograph at night. Before it could fly properly one of the owlets fell from the nest; next morning it was found on the ground below, apparently uninjured. It was placed in a small tree in the Founders quadrangle where its irate mother flew down to guard it. She perched on a

The Spotted Eagle Owl at Bishops: note the ring on her right leg.

nearby branch and refused to leave, indeed it was even possible to catch and ring her. Once released she remained with her owlet, glaring fiercely at anyone who came too near. Thus from a few feet away I was able to obtain my first owl portrait; a standard lens was all that was required this time.

Crossing the Founders quad at night became a dangerous business. If anyone approached too close to her owlet the female swooped down to attack, and when the owls moved to a spot near the housemaster's study these attacks were frequent. As there was a real danger of more serious injury than the occasional raked scalp, we were given an ultimatum by the housemaster to take the young owl 'to a more removèd ground'.

It was at this time that I met Dr G. J. Broekhuysen, who was a lecturer in zoology at the University of Cape Town. He was involved in a detailed study of the Cape Sugarbird, and my bird-watching friends and I were able to assist this project by showing him nests of this species that we had found on the mountain slopes above Kirstenbosch Botanical Gardens during our week-end outings. Dr B, as we called him, had a knack of encouraging the young, especially to record their observations, and I owe much to him for his encouragement during my ornithological nestling period.

Apart from the Cape Sugarbird, the Spotted Eagle Owl was the species next most dear to Dr B's heart, indeed it was he who had come to help us ring the Bishops owl. At the University of Cape Town there was an owl nesting on the ivy-covered lintel over the entrance to the Botany Department and Dr B invited a few of us to come and see it. At the time the behavioural studies of Professor Niko Tinbergen of Oxford were current, and I remember Dr B's excitement when he discovered that the owl had rolled a flash bulb, inadvertently left on the ledge the previous evening, beneath it. Thus it was incubating two eggs and a flash bulb, and Dr B explained to us some of the aspects of instinctive behaviour, of how brooding birds had a compulsion to incubate round objects, and experiments had shown that a gull would attempt to incubate an imitation egg almost too large for it to straddle. That flash bulb rolled into the nest by the owl made Dr B's day—committed behaviourist that he was!

We had seen only the beginning of what was to become a long-term study of the biology of the Spotted Eagle Owl at U.C.T. and elsewhere. Dr B was soon known for his interest in owls through articles in the newspapers, often being called on to inspect owls nesting on buildings and sometimes to advise on what to do when they started to attack people and dogs. I recall going with him to a nest at Fish Hoek where a couple were hosts to an owl breeding outside their bedroom window in a window box intended for geraniums. I was able to lean out of the window and secure a portrait of the owl as she sat with her owlets like some avian Madonna.

Portrait of the female with her owlet in the window-box nest site.

Dr B's pair of Spotted Eagle Owls at U.C.T. obligingly moved to a new nest site where they could be overlooked at a distance from a window in the Zoology department. A powerful light was used to illuminate the nest at night, and the finer details were observed through a telescope. Any student who showed an interest in ornithology was drawn into a team that monitored the behaviour of the owls throughout the night on many occasions. As a result of Dr B's infectious enthusiasm a detailed picture of the breeding biology of the Spotted Eagle Owl was obtained. It was his intention to publish the scientific results on his retirement, and in addition a popular book *It's an Owl's Life* was almost complete. Then, while on holiday in Greece soon after his retirement, Dr B died suddenly after a short illness. It was a tragic loss because so much research was left unpublished. The owl book was also never published, but when I came to write *Birds of Prey of Southern Africa* Mrs Mariette Broekhuysen generously permitted me to draw on the information in her late husband's book for my account of this species.

From Dr B's studies a clear picture of the breeding biology of the Spotted Eagle Owl emerged: the pair remain together for their lifetimes but a lost mate is soon replaced, even during the breeding cycle; most nest sites are on the ground, but a substantial number are in trees or on buildings; eggs are usually laid from August to October; the clutch is two to four eggs, usually two, and they hatch after 30–32 days of incubation; only the female incubates, sitting all day and most of the night except for short breaks when she may be fed by the male; she broods the small chicks closely and the male provides prey which she tears up for them; once the young are about two weeks old she may leave them alone at night and probably assists the male in hunting; the male continues to provide most of the prey, and the female is usually on guard somewhere nearby, even when the chicks are well grown; the young leave the nest after about six weeks, usually before they can fly properly; they are fed by the parents for about another five weeks, then gradually learn to kill for themselves; about two months after leaving the nest the young are independent and they disperse, two ringed juveniles being found at distances of 11 km and 17 km away.

Such are the basics of a Spotted Eagle Owl's life, and a great deal of hard work was required to find out this much. The perennial problem with owls is the difficulty of knowing what they do away from the nest at night. Sometimes one can merely surmise, for example that the female is also hunting because of the increased number of kills or the rapid delivery of prey. But the curtain of darkness beyond the nest means that one's deductions remain of a circumstantial nature.

My experience of the Spotted Eagle Owl remained rather limited until I went to settle in Rhodesia, and I had never photographed at a nest at night.

Eggs of the Spotted Eagle Owl laid on the ground under an overhang; in a hollow in the fork of a gum tree; and in a crow's nest.

Although I had seen quite a number of nests, several of which are illustrated here, the opportunity to photograph the adults at night eluded me. My first Rhodesian nest proved tantalising; it was situated in a hollow on the sheer face of one of the old mine workings at Falcon College but there was nowhere to put up a hide. I had to content myself with a distant picture taken with a 400-mm lens, but at least it illustrated the perfect camouflage of the incubating owl.

Eventually my chance came when Dave Tredgold found a nest at the bottom of his farmhouse garden at Shangani, where I was also soon to photograph Barn Owls in the outbuildings. The Spotted Eagle Owls had chosen to nest on the ground at the base of a large tree and it was an attractive site ideal for photography. The original clutch had been two eggs, but when I set up my hide for photography the nest contained a chick about two weeks old and a recently born hare, presumably killed the previous evening. I was installed in the hide before sunset, and the female returned at dusk. She tore up the hare and fed the owlet, then posed perfectly for her portrait before settling to brood. She remained brooding until Dave came to fetch me from the hide some three hours later; to my disappointment the male had not delivered prey. When I developed the negatives I was delighted with the portraits of the owl with her chick and they remain amongst my favourite black-and-white pictures.

The Shangani Spotted Eagle Owl with her two-week-old owlet, feeding, settling, and brooding.

One day a local farmer arrived at our house at Falcon College with a cardboard box in which he said there was a baby owl; he had shot the parents because he claimed that they were trying to catch his chickens at night. Then he had found the owlet and, smitten with remorse, decided to bring it to me for rearing. The incident had a happy sequel because I was able to convince him of his error in shooting the owls and subsequently he became a keen conservationist as well as a good friend.

When he left I opened the box carefully and sáw two clear yellow eyes set in a downy bundle. As so often when owls are very young it showed no fear. For the time being the box would be sufficient home, far more important was to feed it. I cut up some fresh steak into small pieces which were devoured hungrily. As an owl does not hold food in its crop, I felt between its legs from time to time until the skin of its abdomen was taut, at which stage I knew it was replete. From that moment on, the owlet accepted me as its parent and became imprinted on me. It was christened Isikhova, Ndebele for an owl.

Isikhova was a delightfully amusing pet and lived with us like an addition to the family. A young owl is altogether captivating in its behaviour and a constant source of interest. Isikhova's habit of bobbing his head about when anything caught his attention was extremely comical, and his flexible neck enabled him to get his head into some amazing positions. Once he could stand with confidence, his life took on a new dimension and he made mock kills of any plaything he was given. Later he would flap his wings vigorously and clamber onto the edge of his box, teetering on the brink; it was not difficult to see why owlets so often fell from their nests prematurely.

But there is always a more serious side to keeping a young owl, and I was able to note his feather development as well as learn about his calls. Once his infantile cheeping was abandoned, Isikhova used a ventriloquial wheezing *churrr* as his begging call if he saw me and was hungry. It is a call that carries far and enables the adults to locate their wandering young once they leave the nest. During the day, or when he wasn't hungry, Isikhova used the same call, but with a rather muted sleepy intonation, as a greeting whenever he saw me or I talked to him. If annoyed, for example if someone handled him too roughly, he would clack his bill and emit a high-pitched indignant chittering. The first attempts at hooting were heard about a month after he was able to fly.

Once he could fly Isikhova was never constrained in any way. He used to roost on a horizontal pipe under the eaves at the back of the house, coming to my call each evening to be fed. We also had a regular evening game which developed his hunting skills and gave me an insight into how owls kill in the wild. As soon as he had perched in a tree or on the roof of the house, I would roll a golf ball rapidly over the lawn; Isikhova was ready for this and would swoop down silently and gracefully onto the ball, the click of his claws as he

A portrait of Isikhova.

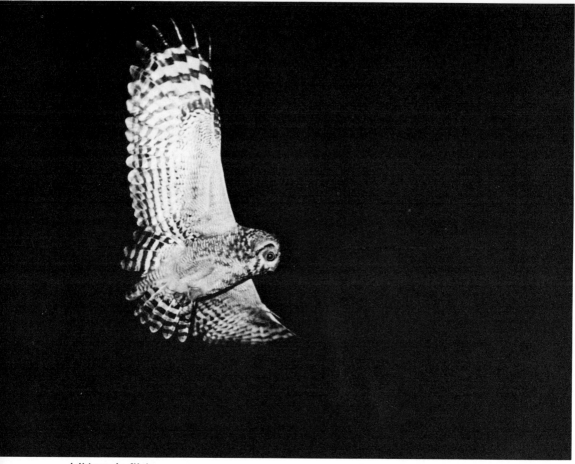

Isikhova in flight.

struck it indicating that he had made a perfect 'kill'. He never tired of this game, and nor did I. Isikhova was the perfect subject for photography and I took many pictures of him, including some in flight, something that would be extremely difficult to do in the wild.

Rearing a wild animal that has no fear of humans always presents problems. The senior English master lived in a cottage behind our house. For some reason his crop of blonde hair fascinated Isikhova, so that when he went abroad at night the owl swooped down to clutch at it. Thus the situation developed that whenever the English master was within a hundred metres or so of his house he would wave his hand, or a ruler, or a book, above his head to ward off the owl's attentions. The schoolboys, of course, found this very amusing. Fortunately he accepted the situation with good humour, but once Isikhova gave him a considerable fright. When he entered his lounge one night and moved slowly forward in the dark to switch on his table lamp, he was greeted by a loud clacking and a hiss. He came over to us, genuinely frightened, to borrow a torch. We returned and shone on the lampshade to find Isikhova perched on it. He had flown in through the front door, left open because of the summer heat, and had made himself at home.

As time went by, Isikhova wandered farther afield, especially once he could catch prey for himself. He returned to roost at the house each day for seven months and then disappeared suddenly. I felt certain that he had met with an accident, but he had been so much part of our lives that I couldn't get him out of my mind. Each morning I would glance up at his roosting perch just in case he was back again. One evening, four months after his disappearance, Isikhova flew into the lounge. He accepted food from me, but no longer allowed me to handle him. He chased his golf ball a couple of times, but then ignored it, as if to say he had cast off such childish things. He remained with us for three days and then disappeared again. Several months later we received the sad news that he had been killed by a car on the road to Bulawayo thirty kilometres away; the ring I had put on his leg when he first learnt to fly identified him beyond doubt and removed all hope that he might return to pay us another visit. The relationship I had with Isikhova had been something special, and the gloom cast by his death lasted a long time. His parents had been shot through ignorance and misunderstanding; Isikhova had died violently because of something his instincts for survival could not comprehend.

Although I had many good pictures of Isikhova, the only nest I had photographed at night while in Rhodesia was the one at Shangani. Here I had concentrated on black-and-white portraits, and the male had not delivered prey; I still envied that photograph of the Bishops owl with the mole in its bill. It looked as if I would have to write this chapter around such pictures as I had, but several years after my return to Cape Town there was an eleventh-hour bonus.

One of my favourite haunts is the Helderberg Nature Reserve at Somerset West, a forty-minute drive from my home in Cape Town. The curator is my friend Nico Myburgh, an outstanding bird-photographer, who thinks like a bird, with the result that his pictures have an innovative quality that few can match. One morning he telephoned to say he had found a Spotted Eagle Owl's nest in a hole in an oak at a height of six metres; it required my pylon hide, so I loaded it and set off for Somerset West. The owls could not have selected a more attractive site in a hole where a branch had rotted away and fresh oak leaves would alleviate the blackness of the background when we photographed with flash at night. The nest contained two young with feathers breaking rapidly through their down; they were about five weeks old, so there was no time to lose. That afternoon we assembled the hide on the ground some distance away, then moved it into position three metres from the nest. When I climbed the nest tree to tie back a few small branches that impeded our view, the female clacked her bill in a nearby oak and then emitted a weird, wailing *kee-ow* hoot in alarm. It was a call that had not been described previously.

The hide was left in place overnight so that the owls could get used to it, and as soon as there was enough light to see the following morning I climbed into it to check that all was well at the nest. Although I did not expect a visit from the adults, I set up my camera and flash to record the doings of the owlets. The hindquarters of a large rat lay in the nest, but the young owls were somnolent and appeared well fed. After about half an hour, just before sunrise, one owlet perked up and turned its attention to the remains of the rat. It picked it up in its bill and attempted to swallow it, but however hard the owlet tried, the hindquarters were just too large for its gape. After various vigorous attempts to gulp it down over a period of about three minutes the rat was dropped. Some while later the process was repeated, then subsequently a further five times. The attempts to swallow the rat were so persistent that there were times when I thought the owlet was going to choke. I recorded the process on film, totally fascinated by its determination, while the other owlet took only a mild interest in the proceedings. Once I was sure that there was no way that the rat could be swallowed I began to dismantle the camera. I withdrew the lens into the hide and, looking out, saw just the tip of the rat's tail protruding from the owlet's bill! It had chosen that moment for a final attempt and had succeeded; there was no time to put the camera back on the tripod so I held it steady and managed to record the conclusion of that Gargantuan meal.

That evening the camera and flashes were set up well before sunset and I began my vigil at 6.30 p.m. The young owls were of a size where they provided plenty of entertainment. They bobbed and weaved their heads about at anything of interest, even a falling leaf, or flapped their wings, or jostled each other as they vied for a turn to perch on the rim of the nest; at no stage was there any animosity between them, and sometimes one would gently nibble the down of the other. Their delightful behaviour brought back vivid memories of Isikhova.

It was more than an hour before the first visit to the nest, and I knew that an adult was in the vicinity by the excited head-bobbing of the owlets. At 7.40 p.m. the female made her first visit, passed something small to a chick, then left. Similar visits were repeated at 8.20, 9.04 and 9.08 p.m. I could not see what was brought and can only assume that they were insects. Although the owl took no notice of the powerful beam of a hunter's torch which illuminated the nest, the visits had been too brief to compose a photograph and I was becoming frustrated. Then at 10.40 p.m., after a long wait, the male landed at the nest, deposited a plucked dove and left. I assumed that it was the male because he approached awkwardly from the side opposite to that regularly used by the female and appeared ill at ease. Shortly afterwards the female came to the nest, tore up the dove, and fed it to her hungry brood. At last I was able to obtain pictures, first of the male, then of the female as she fed the young. Like all birds of prey the contrast between her power and the gentleness with which she tended the owlets was striking. She used a special call, a soft, broody *kapok-kapok-kapok* . . . when 'talking' to her young. After ten minutes the dove had been demolished and she left the nest.

Another hour elapsed before the next visit, this time with a nestling dove which one of the owlets swallowed whole. It was now the witching hour so, appropriately, the male and female indulged in a loud hooting session. They also used a soft bubbling hoot that had a rather conversational quality, a call that I had not heard before. When their hooting ceased the resultant silence was in eerie contrast; if Milton could write of 'darkness visible' then this was silence audible. At 1.15 a.m. she brought a small mouse which was later identified from the photograph as a climbing mouse because of its long tail; it was swallowed whole by one of the owlets. The female remained for a while and attempted to brood her young, not an easy task because of their size, so she sat half in the hole with her wing hanging down, an attractive pose that revealed the subtle pattern of coloration on the open wing. She left after fifteen minutes and did not return until 2.10 a.m., with another small mouse which was again swallowed whole.

At 2.40 a.m. my thirty-year dream came to fruition when the female landed with a mole and posed perfectly with it in her bill before transferring it to her talons and tearing it up for the young. After that feed it was nearly a two-hour wait for the next one, a Laughing Dove which was soon eaten. The final visit was at 5.20 a.m. when it was already light; as if to assure me that I hadn't imagined the first one, she had brought another large mole. Before going to roost for the day the owls had a last loud exchange of hoots.

I ceased observations at 5.30 a.m. after eleven hours in the hide. It had been my intention to leave at about 11 p.m. the previous evening, so I took no food or drink with me. Apart from my hunger and thirst I was also cold and stiff, so stiff in fact that it was only with some difficulty that I was able to climb down the ladder to the ground just six metres below. But all the discomforts were as nothing when weighed against the interest of that night; in all I had had eleven visits, when four insects (presumed), two mice, three doves and two moles were delivered.

Just over a week later, shortly before the young left the nest, I had another session with the owls. This time the young owls were more venturesome and took turns to stand on the rim of the nest and flap their wings vigorously. Despite their size I had seen the female shading them earlier that afternoon when the sun fell on the nest. I was installed at 7 p.m. while it was still light and at 7.23 the female brought a Helmeted Guineafowl chick about a week old which was immediately gulped down whole by one of the owlets. At 7.35 another guineafowl chick was brought and swallowed, then at 7.45 a third one, but when the satiated owlets did not respond she flew off with it, presumably to eat it herself. The three guineafowl chicks were all of the same age and undoubtedly from the same brood; clearly the male or female, perhaps both, had discovered the roost and had systematically plundered it. At 7.52 a small gecko was brought and swallowed whole, then at 8 p.m. a shrew, also swallowed whole. After this feed the female remained with her young for twelve minutes and displayed great affection by nibbling gently in their down while they closed their eyes in pleasure. They were somnolent for some while after she left, but later they perked up and showed a great interest in the moths fluttering round the light of the torch. It was a long wait until 10.22 p.m. when another shrew was brought and immediately swallowed. There followed another period of somnolence, but when the owlets woke up they preened themselves and each other, then took turns on the rim of the nest to exercise their wings. At 1.30 a.m. a small item of unidentified prey was brought and at 2 a.m. I climbed down from the hide. In all there had been seven visits with prey in seven hours and I felt I could not improve on the pictures taken, especially after three consecutive visits with guineafowl chicks.

Thus my experiences with the Spotted Eagle Owl had ended on a high note: my problem was no longer to eke out the pictures I had previously obtained but to decide which of the ones taken at the oak-tree site to select for publication. Then one evening I was asked to show slides to the Ornithological Society at Bishops. The Helderberg owl pictures were included in my presentation and I was delighted to learn that a pair of owls was still in residence at Bishops, although it was not known where they nested. There seems little doubt that the present pair were successors, indeed probably descendants, of the owls I had known so long ago. It gave one a satisfying feeling of continuity. And my story could end where it began.

9: *Cape Eagle Owl*

The Cape Eagle Owl is an elusive species that may easily be overlooked. It has a wide but discontinuous distribution from sea-level in the Cape to the Ethiopian highlands. There are three races: *Bubo capensis capensis* confined to South Africa, *Bubo capensis mackinderi* found from Zimbabwe northwards to the Kenya highlands, and *Bubo capensis dillonii* which occurs in the highlands of Ethiopia and southern Eritrea. Of the three races *capensis* is the smallest, *mackinderi* appreciably larger and *dillonii* intermediate between them. However, the race *dillonii* falls beyond the scope of this account and need not concern us. The largest of the three is sometimes called Mackinder's Eagle Owl, especially in Kenya, and was named after Sir Halford Mackinder, who made the first ascent of Mount Kenya.

As an indication of the elusiveness of the species it was only in 1967 that the first Cape Eagle Owl was recorded in Rhodesia, when one was collected in the Inyanga highlands near the Troutbeck Hotel by the late Ronnie Rankine, notable also for fighting his way free from the jaws of a crocodile that had pulled him into the Zambezi while he was fishing. The second record was a few months later when one was collected in the Matopos hills near Bulawayo. Then in July 1968 I found the first nest in Rhodesia in a cave at Shangani, but ironically I was not aware of the significance of my find until eight years later.

In the decade following the discovery of the Cape Eagle Owl in Rhodesia it was found to be widely but sparingly distributed. There were further records from the Inyanga highlands and a number of breeding pairs were located in the Matopos. In Rhodesia the species showed a marked preference for areas of granite, usually where bare whalebacks, or 'dwalas', were interspersed with wooded valleys. Throughout its range the Cape Eagle Owl occurs mainly in rocky or mountainous terrain, but recently in South Africa it has been recorded in open Karoo habitat, so that its distribution extends farther westwards into a more arid environment than was previously thought suitable. It has also been seen at Vioolsdrift on both sides of the lower Orange River, but nowhere else in Namibia, although in time I predict that it will be found in other localities there—one has only to consider how long it remained un-detected in Rhodesia.

As mentioned in the previous chapter the Cape Eagle Owl can be confused only with the Spotted Eagle Owl. The race *mackinderi*—Mackinder's Eagle Owl—is similar in size to a Giant Eagle Owl, but the latter has dark brown eyes and is a rather uniform pale grey colour. The Cape Eagle Owl may be distinguished from the Spotted by its rufous coloration, by the heavy dark blotching on the breast which forms two 'breast plates', by the orange eyes, by the much broader barring of the feathers of the abdomen and by the much larger feet. It is with the rufous form of the Spotted Eagle Owl that confusion is most likely, indeed I had one of these in captivity for some while before I realised that it was not a Cape Eagle Owl. Its identity was later established by the fine barring on the abdomen and its small feet. In mitigation of my error I should mention that at that stage I had not yet seen a Cape Eagle Owl and did not know that there was a rufous form of the Spotted Eagle Owl.

It was only in the decade after the discovery of the first Rhodesian Cape Eagle Owls that anything worthwhile was published on the species. Two lead-ing ornithologists, Con Benson and Michael Irwin, wrote an important paper on the systematics and distribution of the species in Africa, in which they in-cluded the first two Rhodesian records. This was complemented in 1972 by an excellent account of the biology of the species in Kenya by P. H. B. Sessions, a farmer, who provided yet another example of the value of amateur contribu-tions. In 1973 Richard Brooke summarised the latest-known distribution in Rhodesia and gave an analysis of prey found in a cave in the Matopos. Then in 1976 Val Gargett, best known for her work on Black Eagles in the Matopos, gave a brief summary of breeding pairs discovered there (a more comprehen-sive account was published subsequently). This was followed in the same year by her paper in conjunction with Hans Grobler on the food of the Cape Eagle Owl in the Matopos. In 1977 the decade following the discovery of the species in Rhodesia was rounded off by my own account, in conjunction with Dave Tredgold, of the breeding biology studied at a nest at Shangani. Thus in the short space of ten years the biology of the Cape Eagle Owl advanced from virtually unknown to well known. Subsequently more has been found out, particularly in South Africa, where the species had hardly been studied.

During the day the Cape Eagle Owl roosts in a secluded spot, usually on the ground behind rocks or bushes, and it flushes very reluctantly. This, com-bined with its rugged and often remote habitat, means that it may easily be overlooked, especially as it is rarely killed on roads at night. Once its habitat preferences are known, as well as small clues like the characteristic white splashes of its mutes on bare rocks in the area, it can be located by systematic searching. It was in this way that Val Gargett was able to find seven nests in the Matopos between 1972 and 1977, and subsequently further ones, but this brief comment can give no indication of the physical endurance and dedication involved.

At dusk the owl flies to a prominent perch to watch for prey and then moves on to other vantage points. Its quarry is caught with a swift, silent swoop and killed with the powerful talons. Throughout its range the Cape Eagle Owl preys mainly on a locally abundant prey species. In his Kenya study Sessions found that mole-rats predominated in one area, dassies in another, while in southern Africa red rock hares are most frequently preyed on. At most nest sites or roosts large ossuaries are built up and prey may be identified from these bone fragments. In their study of prey from sites in the Matopos Gargett and Grobler analysed 925 prey items according to their estimated original weight. They found that 99 per cent of the total weight of prey was mammalian, the balance being made up with some birds, insects, scorpions and lizards. Of the mammals, red rock hares comprised 63 per cent of the total, while dassies and scrub hares made up a further 23 per cent. It is worth mention that the skulls of the rock hares were usually intact except for the cranial and nasal areas, which were characteristically broken off by the owl; this greatly facilitated the identification of remains. Although on a very

Skulls of red rock hares with the cranial and nasal areas characteristically broken off by a Cape Eagle Owl.

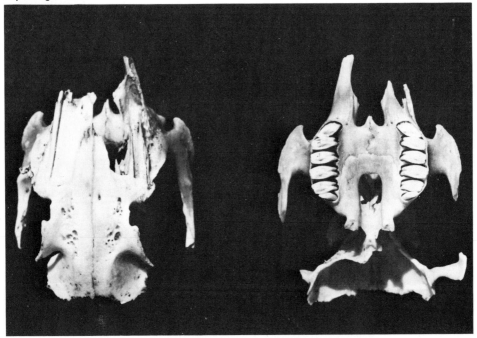

much smaller scale, we found the same basic pattern of prey preferences at the nest studied at Shangani. Subsequently these preferences were confirmed at nests found by Hans Grobler near Cradock in South Africa, the first substantial analysis of prey of the Cape Eagle Owl south of the Limpopo. He was able to locate nest sites by drawing on his experience of the species in Rhodesia.

The partiality of the Cape Eagle Owl for one type of prey does not mean that it does not take other items as opportunity arises. In their Matopos study Gargett and Grobler recorded sixteen mammal and seven bird species, as well as a few invertebrates and lizards. The owls also provided an interesting new locality record for the Lesser Cane-rat, known previously from only two other localities in Rhodesia. One of the features of their study was the close association between the prey recorded and the granite kopje environment. In Kenya Sessions found his owls to be partial to freshwater crabs, whose remains he came across in a quarter of the pellets he examined. That the Cape Eagle Owl has an adaptable diet is revealed from an analysis of prey from a nest at Brandvlei in the north-west Cape during a prolonged period of drought. The owls fed mainly on invertebrates such as insects and scorpions, as well as on geckos, otherwise on a few birds and small mammals. The largest prey item was a young hare.

The breeding biology of the Cape Eagle Owl, although only recently studied, is now fairly well known. Courtship involves increased hooting, the male bowing to the female with his white throat patch puffed out at each hoot, an effective visual signal in the dark. The nest is always in a secluded position, on the ground or on a ledge or in a cave with a drop below, and is well concealed behind rocks or bushes. No nest as such is made, but the owl usually makes a shallow scrape in the earth if the situation permits. Although it is said in some textbooks to breed in the stick nests of raptors and crows, no authentication of this has been provided. However, in Kenya Sessions found nests on low tree stumps, and in one case in the fork of a tree fifteen metres above ground. The same site may be used year after year, although the owls may move to an alternate site after a breeding failure. The normal clutch is two eggs, but occasionally one or three are laid. In southern Africa eggs are laid from late May to August. The eggs of Mackinder's Eagle Owl are markedly larger than those of the Spotted Eagle Owl, enabling them to be identified on size alone, but in South Africa the eggs of the smaller race of the Cape Eagle Owl are not consistently larger. Because of this overlap in size with the Spotted Eagle Owl, extreme care in identifying the eggs is needed.

The subsequent details of the breeding biology of the Cape Eagle Owl may best be incorporated in the story of the nest I studied at Shangani. I mentioned earlier that there was an eight-year lag before I realised I had found the first Rhodesian nest, and this requires some explanation. In June 1968 I camped with a party of my pupils from Falcon College at Wabai Hill on Debshan Ranch. Our purpose was to investigate the only known breeding site of the Cape Vulture north of the Limpopo. They bred on the southern face of a huge granite whaleback in otherwise open ranching country. Breeding was first confirmed there in 1965, and then sporadically until 1971, but not since. The reasons for the failure of the Wabai Hill vultures to breed successfully are rather obscure and speculative, but on that visit we made a count of sixty-two vultures and thought that one nest was occupied, although this could not be confirmed. Our main task complete, we decided to explore the outlying portions of the Wabai Hill complex for anything of interest, including Bushman paintings. After a while we came across a narrow amphitheatre of bare rock which encircled an area of thick woodland. Along one side were several pothole caves which we decided to investigate. On reaching one of these some seven metres from the base of the cliff, we flushed an owl which flew over the valley and disappeared into thick cover. We found the two white eggs at the base of a Paper Tree and I assumed that they belonged to a Spotted Eagle Owl. My notes for 7 June 1968 recorded it as such and there the matter rested.

I remained oblivious to the importance of my find until 1974, when I saw my first Cape Eagle Owl (actually my second, but my glimpse in 1968 hardly counts!). In that year Val Gargett took me to one of her nests, and the owl flew across the valley to perch on the other side. I was able to look my fill, but the features that struck me most were the orange eyes and the huge feet. Soon after the owl alighted it was molested by a pair of White-necked Ravens; they walked round and round the owl uttering hoarse imprecations and even jumped over it a few times. The owl was incapable of effective retaliation, although it did once jump towards them with bared talons, and the ravens easily won the confrontation, which lasted all of ten minutes.

The following weekend Val took me to another nest site which was strikingly similar to that at Shangani; the three eggs were even laid near the base of a Paper Tree. I had already been thinking back to 1968, but the visit to this site confirmed in my mind that the habitat and nest site at Shangani indicated a Cape and not a Spotted Eagle Owl.

It was not until the 1976 breeding season that an opportunity arose to visit the Shangani site. Dave Tredgold had recently moved from Meikles ranch to take over as manager of Debshan. As was his habit Dave had explored much of his new domain on foot, so when I described the amphitheatre in which the owls had nested he found it without too much difficulty. On 6 June 1976 he rang me to say that he had seen two large owls in the late afternoon perched together on the rock face below the nest site. The signs were encouraging because Sessions had observed that prior to breeding the pair may be seen perching near each other.

Thick woodland surrounded by bare granite slopes: typical Cape Eagle Owl habitat in the Matopos.

The first Cape Eagle Owl I saw was mobbed by two White-necked Ravens.

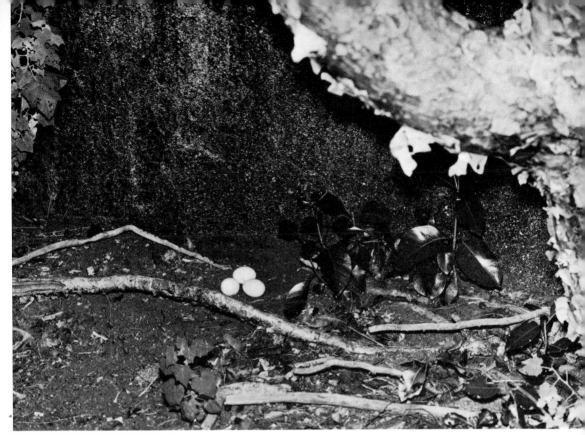

Nest of a Cape Eagle Owl in the Matopos.

A young Cape Eagle Owl in a nest near Betty's Bay; a mole and a Barn Owl lie in the nest.

The following weekend I set off with Graeme Arnott for Shangani. It was my hope that he could get a good view of an owl because he was working on the plates for my book on birds of prey and had never seen a Cape Eagle Owl. Soon after arriving at the ranch we set off with Dave. We parked the Land Rover at the entrance to the amphitheatre and then made our way through thick bush to the nest site. The climb up to the cave was less formidable than it appeared, as long as one had shoes with soft rubber soles and the ability to find what mountaineers call 'friction grips', a purchase on granite that is sometimes rather more fictional than frictional! Anyway, we reached the cave without too much difficulty, and an owl flew out from the back of the ledge to perch in the fork of a tree in the woodland below. She adopted a crouching position, raised her ear tufts and half-closed her eyes. Had we not taken careful note of where she alighted she would have been very difficult to detect. We all looked our fill, especially Graeme, and then he made a perfect quick sketch of her, an ability that I greatly admire and envy. I inspected the ledge and found a nest scrape at the base of a large tussock-like sedge. The nest was just two metres away from the previous site at the base of the Paper Tree, where she had also made a tentative scrape, and it was gratifying to find the owl still there eight years later to rectify my original error. We did not stay long in case our presence might upset the owl. As we moved down the valley we heard a series of resonant *coo-cook* hoots, a mellow sound like the call of a Speckled Pigeon, quite different from the hoot of a Spotted Eagle Owl.

Now that the error of my original misidentification had been laid to rest, I hoped to study the breeding cycle of the owls and obtain overnight observations and photographs, something never before attempted with this species. Thus it was with some trepidation that I visited the nest with Dave on the evening of 19 June, a week after our previous visit. What if the owl had taken exception and moved off elsewhere? To our relief we flushed the female and found a single fresh egg in the nest. I measured the egg and then we left quickly so as to keep disturbance to a minimum. We did not visit the nest again until 3 July when two eggs were found; I measured the second egg and again we left quickly. On all our visits the female sat extremely tight, crouching low with her eyes mere slits, then she would leave via a tunnel between the sedge clumps at the back of the nest. She usually flew into cover in the valley below, but once she perched in view and hooted, puffing her white throat out conspicuously with each hoot. At no time did we see the male and we were never able to find out where he roosted. An interesting point is that we never found any signs of prey during the incubation period, which indicated that the female probably left the nest cave to feed. One can only surmise that the male may incubate briefly while she is away.

When we visited the nest on the evening of 23 July we found a small chick

View of the nest site (arrowed) in a cave at Shangani, where I photographed the Cape Eagle Owl at night.

estimated to be a day old and the eggshells still lay in the nest. If the single egg was fresh when first found, then the incubation was thirty-four days, the first time it has been obtained in southern Africa, although Sessions estimated it to be about thirty-six days in Kenya. Our findings were gratifyingly similar in view of the difficulties in establishing such information with precision. The second egg hatched four days after the first, which one may assume to be the actual laying interval if incubation began with the first egg.

The owlets were rather comical in appearance, mainly because of their disproportionately large heads and tightly closed eyes; their pink flesh was sparsely covered with off-white down. It was convenient to give them names to distinguish them during the subsequent study, so the larger was named Festus, the smaller one Gomes, after characters in a comedy television programme then current. I was interested to see that a young dassic found in the nest with the day-old chick was still there three days later when the second chick hatched. At this stage a single large kill could last several days, a situation which did not apply towards the end of the nestling period.

On 30 July, when the chicks were eight and four days old, we visited the nest to erect a hide. This presented problems because the cave was not large and there was no other position except flush against one wall two metres from the nest. Before we departed we weighed and measured the owlets; Festus was 220 g, Gomes 80 g, and the first quills were just visible on Festus's back. Their eyes were still closed. We were not unduly worried that Gomes was a third of the weight of Festus because two dassies lay in the nest, more than enough for several owlets, and the feathers of a Speckled Pigeon scattered round the nest provided evidence of a previous meal. We withdrew to watch for the return of the owl. It was late afternoon, when we made most of our visits so that the owl would be encouraged to return quickly under the cover of approaching dusk. I was worried about the closeness of the hide to the nest, and wondered if the owl would be frightened off by the dummy lens and flash that we had put in place. We had already decided that if the owl did not return soon after sunset we would quickly go up and remove the hide. After about fifteen minutes the female flew to the cave but left almost immediately. It appeared that the hide was not to her liking but we decided to watch a little longer. Ten minutes later she returned; it seemed an eternity as the first minute passed, then the next, but after twenty minutes, when it was almost too dark to see, she was still in the cave. It was with an intense sense of relief that we made our way back to the Land Rover.

Late the following afternoon Dave installed me in the hide. The female flew from the nest when we arrived and we found the remains of one dassie on the nest. It was doubtful whether the chicks could have eaten all of the other one, so presumably the female had also fed off it. We weighed Festus and Gomes and found that they had gained 32 per cent and 15 per cent in weight respectively since the previous evening. Before Dave left me I made sure everything was in readiness because I was committed to a long night in the cave; once he was gone I could not emerge from the hide to adjust anything. It was also important to ensure that nothing inside the hide could make a noise, such as a thermos being knocked over, and I had packed my sandwiches in a cloth so that I could unwrap them in silence. The proximity of the hide to the nest meant that nothing could be left to chance.

My vigil began at 5.30 p.m. when Dave left. Soon afterward two White-necked Ravens landed on the lip of the ledge, presumably to try to filch scraps of food. The incident illustrated a potential hazard for the owls because they could easily have killed and eaten the chicks. The ravens precipitated the return of the female within ten minutes and they flew off as she approached. She came to the nest and glared at the hide, her vivid orange eyes seeming to bore through the fabric. I dared not take a picture lest she flew off, so I merely looked in awe at one of the most impressive and powerful owls I had yet seen. After a while she stopped glaring and settled to brood her chicks. Never before, or since, have I exercised so much self-control while photographing a bird. I sat a mere two metres from an owl never before photographed at the nest and had to force myself to keep my shaking fingers off the cable release. As the mantle of darkness settled around the cave, I heard a Boubou Shrike cursing like a rusty ratchet in the woodland below and a Freckled Nightjar gave vent to its distinctive *wow-wow* call, like a small terrier yapping in the distance. After twenty minutes I could hold back no longer. The owl was brooding with Festus protruding from beneath her as I released the shutter; to my relief she didn't even start and this boldness characterised all her subsequent behaviour.

From time to time I heard soft chittering calls from the chicks, but they had also already developed a wheezing begging call virtually identical to that of a young Spotted Eagle Owl. However, it was not until 7.40 p.m. that powerful scrunching sounds indicated that the chicks were being fed. I switched on the torch that was focused on the nest and watched the process, impressive in its sheer power as she ripped up the prey. At one stage the female picked up the young dassie bodily in her bill. Once the young had been fed she settled to brood them again. The night passed uneventfully, punctuated occasionally by the eerie alarm calls of dassies, possibly because the male was in the area, but I did not see or hear him. So I measured out my night with cups of tea and a sandwich from time to time; during a long watch when time passes so slowly such events take on an importance far beyond their nutritional value. Something that I found surprising was the warmth in the cave, for I had gradually been peeling off the layers of clothing I had

Cape Eagle Owl brooding her small chick.

The female with a young dassie in her bill.